# The Craft Distillers' Handbook

First published in Great Britain 2015 by
Lovely Moon Publishing.
This second edition published in 2017 by
Posthouse Publishing Ltd, No 2 Cleat, St Margaret's Hope, South Ronaldsay,
Orkney, KW17 2RW.
© Posthouse Publishing Ltd and Lovely Moon Publishing

A CIP catalogue for this book is available from the British Library
ISBN 978 1 903872 37 6
10 9 8 7 6 5 4 3

**Disclaimer:** The publishers have made every effort to ensure the accuracy of information in the book
at the time of going to press. However, they cannot accept responsibility for any loss, injury or
inconvenience resulting from the use of information contained in this book.

### Author acknowledgements
Many people have helped in the preparation of this book, not least the craft distillers who have
submitted themselves to being interviewed as case studies. My heartfelt thanks are also due to
Dominic Roskrow, Bob Donaldson, Laurence Conisbee, Tom Warner, Sion Edwards, Harriet Roe,
Mike Hardingham, James Young, and Vanessa van Heerden.  I would also like to thank Alan Powell
for his input on HMRC legislation included in this second edition. If I have forgotten anybody, my
sincerest apologies.

Printed and bound in Great Britain by T.J. International Ltd.

# The Craft Distillers' Handbook

## SECOND EDITION

**A practical guide to making and marketing spirits**

Ted Bruning

# Contents

# Foreword

As an independent distiller for some 16 years we have experienced most of the challenges faced when building a premium brand from commissioning a still to exporting across the globe. There are a number of issues to consider when developing a new craft distillery.

What kind of scale do you want to achieve? Scale matters if you want a long-term viable business as opposed to a hobby. You need a strong vision and an awful lot of patience to make the journey. Building both quality stock and a loyal customer base are equally challenging

Are visitors part of the plan? Our Visitor Centre has become an important part of our business with its shop, tours and masterclasses. Yes it's a good outlet for sales, but more importantly it's the best brand building vehicle you've got – a chance to tell your story really well.

Are you serving a local market? Back in the early 2000s local support was essential for us. We created a club for members who quickly became ambassadors for the brand. The business has grown but our members are still highly valued. Starting as a regional brand allows you to create a strong presence on a manageable scale and can lead to bigger and better listings. Further afield, do you have ambitions overseas? Attracting and setting up arrangements with importers is time-consuming, but essential for brand growth and long term viability.

What scale of business will your cash resources allow? Cash is always king in any business but in a distillery it is more challenging than your average start-up.

Is it all about the brand? As craft distillers we are unlikely to be able to compete with the 'big boys' for advertising spend, so how can we get noticed? The two main ways we define ourselves are taste and stories. It is vital to get people nosing and tasting our products. We regularly have a presence at whisky fairs, as well as tasting tables at high profile functions like sporting and artistic events.

Finally we come to stories. Single malt whisky and good stories go hand-in-hand. This is especially true as the numbers of distilleries increase as everyone needs a point of difference. Fortunately our distillery has many stories we can draw on.

In this digital era, viral videos, social media posts, press releases and direct marketing are all harnessed to tell our stories. At a time when we are bombarded by news and information on all sides, a compelling and engaging story will always find a reader.

Stephen Davies, Chief Executive, Penderyn Distillery
May 2017

# Introduction

It's a seductive vision. You... in control of a gleaming copper pot-still, the wash seething away merrily inside it, with the birth of a few hundred bottles of delicately-scented gin or rich, heady whisky only hours away. A solid, well-founded business making a unique spirit that you can take real pride in, earning the respect and applause of connoisseurs the world over, and with a happily healthy balance-sheet to boot – what's not to like?

If that's your vision, it's one you share with a rapidly growing number of people: people who crave independence, but who will only settle for an occupation they can take genuine pride in; people with the craftsman's capacity for taking infinite pains over the minutest detail, yet with the entrepreneur's grasp of the broader and more distant horizons too.

## A growing sector

It would be an exaggeration to say that small-scale artisanal distilling was spreading through the country like wildfire; but after what looked almost like a false start in the 1980s it has gathered pace at a remarkable rate in the last 15 years. The exact number of start-ups in that time is hard to know, since Her Majesty's Revenue & Customs doesn't keep (or claims not to keep) a central record of new licences issued; but it must be 50 or 60, with more popping up like mushrooms wherever you look. This is nothing like the rate of start-ups in the microbrewing sector, and is probably slower than the rate of expansion in craft cidermaking; but there's more to it than raw numbers. For in terms of capital investment, it's more than merely impressive: it's almost breathtaking. An entry-level whisky distillery, according to one consultant, will cost an absolute minimum of £100,000 to equip, and some quite modest entrants have invested two or three times that. Cotswold Distillery near Banbury came in at £2,000,000, with a further £2,500,000 scheduled. Compare that to the £25,000 which will buy and equip a perfectly viable microbrewery – even less for a cider mill – and the true scale and significance of the craft distilling industry becomes more apparent.

Not for the faint-hearted, then, or the impulsive. Still, to put matters into context, it need cost no more to establish your own distillery than it would to buy a seaside bed and breakfast, or an independent car repair business, or a country pub. And, unlike those businesses, craft distillers have the comfort of knowing they're in a sector which is actually growing. It has been greatly helped by the fact that between 1997 and 2007 the duty on spirits was frozen, while the duty on beer and wine increased in line with inflation. The duty on a unit of spirits in 2012-13 – 24p – was still much higher than the duty per unit on beer at 17p and wine at 18p, but the differential has been so seriously eroded that a single measure of a standard spirit in a pub is now cheaper than a pint of session-strength bitter, whereas before 1997 it was very much higher.

Even so, the growth in sales of spirits is somewhat counterintuitive given both the economic situation and the fact that the mainstream retail trade, both on- and off-licensed, remains effectively closed to newcomers. The secret of the sector's success, duty notwithstanding, lies in two factors, one as old as time and one brand-spanking new. The first is that no matter how hard times may be for most people, the well-off are as well off as ever – better off, in truth – and their demand for top-quality goods and services of all sorts, including fine spirits and the high-end hotels, restaurants, and wine merchants that sell them, remains largely undiminished. The second is that internet trading sidesteps the mainstream retail trade altogether. Tesco and JD Wetherspoon may have no space on their shelves for your handcrafted eau-de-vie de framboise; but anybody with access to the net and enough credit on their plastic can buy it, and without even having to leave the comfort of their own home. Some craft distillers are already beginning to mutter darkly that there can only be room for so many brands of hand-crafted gin on the market; but no new distillery has gone bust yet (compare this to the microbrewing sector at the equivalent stage of its evolution, when half of those who had started up had already shut down again!), and with the more or less free marketing and national distribution that the internet provides, there's no reason why anyone even moderately competent ever should.

## Where do craft distillers come from?

Similarities are often drawn between craft distilling and microbrewing but turn out, on inspection, to be more apparent than real. One great difference is that the pioneering microbrewers were in many cases middle-aged mainstream brewers who had lost their jobs during the great waves of rationalisation that saw more than half of the brewing plants in the country close down. All these gentry knew was how to brew; all they had was their redundancy money; it was inevitable that many of them were going to put the two together, if only because it was the only way they could think of to make their living. Today's craft distillers are different. Fewer of them have a background in the industry and few, if any, of them have been pushed into their new vocation by need. Nor is there that all-pervading sense among craft distillers, as there always has been among microbrewers, that the mainstream industry has debased the product in the name of Mammon and that its misdeeds have to be corrected by people of purer motives and higher ideals. If anything the reverse is true: the innovations that the big mainstream companies have been introducing to their own portfolios and marketing in recent years, especially in vodka and whisky, have fed the consumers' appetite for both quality and novelty, and it's from the ranks of these energised consumers that many of the new-wave distillers have emerged. Perhaps as a result there seems to be none of the rancour between mainstream distiller and newcomer that once – and to the detriment of the whole industry – soured relations between the old-established family brewers and the parvenu micros.

To take the dissimilarities one step further, a great bone of contention between large and small brewers was the established brewers' monopolistic stranglehold over the pub trade through the tie and, in the "free" trade, tied loans. Microbrewers were desperate for local trade, which they were barred from; in response, they had to develop a nationwide distribution system of independent wholesalers to get access to what genuine free trade there was, which took years; and then, after the 1990 Beer Orders more or less dismantled the biggest tied estates, batter at the doors of the successor pub companies for admission – a process which, again, took years. Thanks to the internet, the problem has more or less disappeared and craft distillers face far less formidable obstacles in getting at their consumers than did the pioneering microbrewers of 30 years ago.

## HMRC unbends

As if this picture wasn't already suspiciously rosy, HM Revenue & Customs is now prepared to give fair and prompt consideration to all new applications within its overall framework for excise approvals. In the 1980s when Bertram Bulmer and Julian Temperley founded, respectively, the King Offa and Somerset Royal cider brandy distilleries, HM Customs & Excise (as it then was) was perfectly accustomed to licensing the new builds, mostly in Scotland, of big distillery conglomerates whose capacity fluctuated according to world demand. Allt-a-Bhainne, Auchroisk, Braeval – these applications for new licences went through if not exactly on the nod, certainly with a minimum of fuss. From 2000 on more and more small independent distilleries were clamouring for licences; and as the legislation that governed licensing was flexible enough to answer the demand it only remained for HMRC to be equally flexible. To everyone's astonishment, it has proved not merely flexible but – by Civil Service standards, admittedly – positively gymnastic; and HMRC is now doing its best to walk beside you rather than trying to bar your way.

So there you are: rising demand, good access to market, co-operative officialdom... there is no reason, provided you have the money to invest, why you should not set up the still you've been dreaming of. The devil, though, is in the detail; and what this book sets out to do is to lay out some of the detail wherein the devil resides. It will not teach you how to distill, although it will point you towards people who will. Rather, it will give you a picture of the scale and nature of the challenges that lie between you and your dream, and help you to make up your mind whether the prey is worth the pursuit.

# 01

# The Opportunity

Investing in a distillery is an expensive and complicated business, a prospect that until recently has put off many people who might have liked the idea of making their own gin or liqueurs. The traditional view of Customs as being implacably opposed to the opening of new distilleries has only added another layer of doubt. But the appearance in the last five years alone of over a 100 new distilleries, mainly small, artisanal affairs, should be enough to prove that here is a viable business that, for many categories of investor, is well worth seriously considering.

## Recession and opportunity

One attraction is that premium and super-premium spirits are virtually recession-proof. It's an industry commonplace that in hard times people drink less but better; and like many such commonplaces, it's not entirely true but is a good enough rule of thumb. What actually happens is that as the poor get poorer they both reduce their consumption and migrate to value brands, so sales of standard brands decline. But the well-off mysteriously tend to get better off, so the market share of premium and super-premium brands increases. Not their actual sales, note – just their share of the market.

To illustrate the point: HMRC obligingly separates whisk(e)y clearances from those of other spirits in its bulletins. Between 2008, the year of the credit crunch, and 2015 Britain's overall consumption of spirits, both domestic and imported, fell from 1,154,368 hectolitres of pure alcohol to 1,119,431hlpa, a 3.3 per cent decline. Over the same period sales of whisk(e)y fell much further, from 296,016hlpa to 237,834hlpa or 19.6 per cent, as less well-off consumers switched to cheaper alternatives or simply bought less alcohol. But sales of the much more expensive single malt whisky actually went up from 32,544hlpa to 34,458hlpa, a

5.5 per cent increase comfortably ahead of both the market's overall performance and the whisk(e)y category as a whole. (A hectolitre of pure alcohol comes to a sniff over 350 70cl bottles at 40 per cent alcohol by volume).

Perhaps it's a bit of a statement of the obvious to say that in tough times, the rich keep spending while the poor tighten their belts. But the fact that demand for premium products tends to remain pretty steady even when the economy slows down is one of the reasons why a recession is a good time to start a business dealing in top-of-the-range spirits such as malt whiskies, premium gins, exquisite liqueurs and artisanal specialities.

## Business discipline

A business established in a recession is likely to be a robust one where costs are under tight control and governance in all areas – human resources, credit periods, cash flow – is likely to be strict. Sales and marketing are likely to be innovative, energetic and proactive. And with such a lean and hungry foundation, any business that can become profitable in hard times should become super-profitable when the trading environment improves.

Recessions tend to bring out the entrepreneur in people who might have been sitting out the good times in cosy jobs on apparently secure salaries: the looming possibility of redundancy has persuaded many people to turn their pipe dream into a business plan. It's remarkable, in fact, how much of the capital that fuelled the microbrewing boom in its early years came from redundancy cheques and downsizing. It was a long time before the banks cottoned on to the fact that while a microbrewery wasn't going to make anyone rich, the rate of business failure in the sector was comparatively low (and of the microbreweries that have closed since the early years, very few have done so through insolvency) and started lending. But that doesn't seem to have deterred many would-be microbrewers – one of the most famous was launched on a string of credit cards and a loan from the brewer's mum.

And recessions tempt existing businesses to investigate ways of diversifying into new but synergetic areas of operation. To pursue the microbrewing analogy further, many free-of-tie publicans have installed a brewing plant in their outbuildings – in more than one case, in what had been the outside loo. One Courage tenant founded a brewery in an old cooperage across the road from his pub just to supply fellow tied lessees with the guest ales the new Beer Orders permitted them to stock. It became so successful that he gave up the tenancy to concentrate on brewing: the brewery celebrates its silver anniversary in 2015.

As we have seen, though, the similarities between those pioneering microbrewers and the new wave of craft distillers are more apparent than real. The majority of the first microbrewers were actually refugees from the mainstream industry, thrown back on their own resources by the massive concentration of production capacity in 1960s and '70s. Some of them had been pretty senior figures before they found themselves rationalised out of a job, so they went into business with a great deal of practical knowledge, understanding of the trade and networks of contacts already in the bag. Furthermore, many of them only founded breweries of their own because, as middle-aged professionals (late middle-aged, in some cases!) with no experience of other industries, they more or less had to. The times were economically parlous then as well, remember (when aren't they!), and jobs were thin on the ground.

None of these statements applies to the pioneer cadre of the craft distilling revival; or at least not to a significant number of them. They haven't, by and large, brought any great hands-on experience of distilling, and few of them appear to be driven by need or the fear of imminent need.

They are, in a sense, more hard-headed: they have spotted a good business opportunity in a fascinating area of endeavour and have determined to exploit it. If that all sounds a little cold, though, craft distilling is not without its romance and that is undoubtedly part of the attraction.

So what is the opportunity that all these hard-headed businesspeople have spotted? Or rather, what are the opportunities; and, more importantly, who is best-placed to exploit and profit from them?

## International brand-builders

The people best-placed to benefit from venturing into the spirits business are (as always) likely to be well-capitalised and well-connected marketing professionals with strong international links; for although domestic sales of spirits faltered during the recession, the export markets tell a very different story. In 2000, Britain exported a healthy-looking 3,273,587 litres of potable spirits. By 2007, the year before the credit crunch, exports had climbed substantially, to 4,321,182 litres. So did they go into decline as the world tightened its belt? Did they heck as like! In 2013, they reached 7,346,295 litres, and at time of writing the outturn for 2017 looked set to top a staggering 1.5 billion litres, according to the Wine & Spirit Trading Association. So, plenty of scope there.

### Scotch worldwide

Exports of Scotch have risen so hugely that the industry is getting seriously worried about the possibility of failing to meet demand. In the calendar year 2016, exports of Scotch whisky increased in value by £153 million to more than £4 billion (£4,008,927,149), and by volume to the equivalent of more than 1.2bn bottles – an increase of 4 per cent and 4.8 per cent respectively. This is the first time since 2011 that both value and volume of Scotch exports recorded positive annual growth rates, and the first time ever that single malt exports have exceeded £1bn. But bottled blended Scotch whisky is still by far the biggest category. It accounted for 69 per cent of all Scotch volumes and values exported in 2016.

Several new distilleries both large and small have opened in the past five years and 30 more are being planned. For the most part, these are being built by the major distilleries to produce 'filling' – malt whisky intended for blending rather than single malts – but quite a number of artisanal malt distilleries such as Loch Ewe, Abhainn Dearg, Kilchoman and Daftmill have appeared too, and more are in the pipeline. These smaller ventures may start out with their eyes firmly fixed on the home market, but even if they don't seek export sales, they inevitably find that export sales seek them. American enthusiasts in particular prize novelties and rarities, the more obscure the better, and avidly exchange news of their gustatory triumphs on social media.

## Gin exports

If whisky has been leading the export charge, gin has not been far behind. Sophisticated cocktail bars, which are on the increase in all the key world markets, have an insatiable thirst for gins of all kind. While the major manufacturers such as Diageo, William Grant, Pernod Ricard and Greenalls have been rushing out well-promoted (and, according to independent reviewers, extremely well-made) premium and super-premium brands, they have left plenty of room for the independent sector. Some of the biggest independent brands in the export markets are contract-distilled, such as Bulldog, produced at G&J Greenall in Warrington, Juniper Green Organic Gin, produced at Thames Distillers in South London, and Broker's London Dry, produced at the Langley Distillery in Birmingham. The fact that the owners of these brands are essentially marketeers who contract out the actual production doesn't equate to the bandwagon-jumping of corner-cutting big brewers who label cheaply-produced everyday beers as 'craft' in the hope of fooling enough of the people for enough of the time: the consumers of super-premium spirits know their stuff and, for £40 and northwards a bottle, insist on the very finest, while the contract distillers who make the spirit are expert small-batch producers of several generations' standing.

But the true artisans – those who make their own gin on their own stills – are by no means excluded from the world markets. Chase of Worcestershire exports a third of its output while gins from Sipsmiths of West London, surely the most media-savvy of the new-wave craft distillers, are on sale in 15 countries. But export markets are hard work for small players: establishing trustworthy agents, finding reliable carriers, processing the paperwork of different jurisdictions, networking with trade customers – these are all difficult and often burdensome areas for businesses whose time is severely rationed.

## Existing drinks producers

Among those who are best-placed to succeed as distillers are those who are already brewing beer or making wine or cider. It was, after all, two cidermakers deciding to distill their own brandy that kicked the whole thing off. The advantages here are practical ones. Not only have existing producers already taken the first step by producing fermented liquor to feed their stills with, they have also developed a network of distributors and almost certainly retailers as well. And they already have a name: consumers know who they are and have an idea of the quality of their existing products that will encourage them to try anything new. And if they already have a product to sell then they already have cash-flow, and they already have working relationships with their banks, with their local authorities and with HMRC. Finally, it almost goes without saying that they already have premises. With all the horrors of the start-up period out of the way, they have more time and energy to pour into making and selling their new products.

## Brewers

Brewers, in theory, ought to have been among the leaders of the craft distilling revival. Merely by omitting the hops they already produce the raw material for either gin or whisky. More than almost any other trade, they have direct access to their retail base. And with the number of microbreweries now comfortably approaching the 2,000 mark but the number of real ale outlets dwindling by the week they, more than anyone, ought to be looking for new ideas to keep the show on the road. But until Adnams of Southwold suddenly burst out of its cocoon with its huge new shiny all-purpose distillery, brewery involvement in craft distilling had been surprisingly limited. St Austell half-owns and makes the wash for the Hicks & Healey distillery in Cornwall; Brains of Cardiff made the wash for Penderyn until it installed its own mashtun; and Liverpool Organic Brewery is a partner in a gin distillery (see below). Other than that marginal involvement, the brewing industry seems to be happy in its comfort zone. But its comfort zone is rapidly shrinking, and although Adnams of Southwold has so far been the only established brewer to plunge wholeheartedly into the spirit world, distilling seems a natural direction of travel for brewers both large and small.

## Winemakers

Winemakers, too, surely ought to be looking to diversify into distilling. Brandy is one of the most popular spirits on the planet; and what's brandy, after all, but distilled wine? Winemaking is growing both in quantity and quality in

England and Wales, and our sparkling white wines have beaten genuine Champagne in so many comparative blind tastings it's embarrassing. Still, no English winemaker would confess to being rolling in money: the fact that the acreage under vines and the number of entrants to the industry are on the increase doesn't affect the bottom lines of those already in the business. If distilling some of their output added value, why wouldn't they want to do it?

Well, two reasons. The first and most obvious is that few if any English vineyards produce anything like enough wine to set aside for distilling, which swallows up very considerable quantities; and what they do produce is high-grade stuff that sells at a good price. The distilling process will concentrate the wine by a factor of 10, so every case of wine you could have sold for £65 – £70 wholesale will make you a bottle-and-a-bit of brandy that you might sell for £30 wholesale. These figures are, of course, very approximate; but they could be out by a margin of 25 per cent and you could still be making a loss. And that's without taking even the cash-flow implication of maturation and the duty differential between spirits and table wines into account.

The second reason is that only really bad grapes make really good brandy. The Ugni Blanc that accounts for 90 per cent of the plantings in the Cognac region is very acid and produces a wine that's lower in alcohol than cheap Liebfraumilch – say 7–9 per cent alcohol. Ugni Blanc or, to give it its original Italian name, Trebbiano Toscano, doesn't perform as badly as that everywhere: if it did it wouldn't be so widely planted. But in the ungenerous soil of the Cognac region it does, and that's what the brandy distillers want. English winemakers, obviously, don't plant that kind of grape, and it would have to be a pretty poor year, even by our standards, that produced a vintage bad enough for brandy. Having said that, Ludlow Vineyard now has its own distillery and produces brandy using poor-quality grapes, the vintages of bad years, and the surpluses from bumper years; but the scale of its capital investment means that it makes apple brandy and eau de vie as well as grape brandy, and to keep the pot full it also distills for other vineyards.

That's not the end of it, though. There is always marc or grappa. Only the most ruthless winemakers press every last drop out of their grapes. The pomace – the mass of skins and pulp left over after pressing – is more than merely moist: it contains juice that need not go to waste. Red wine is fermented on the pomace to extract the pigment from the skins, so the juice pressed from this will already be alcoholic and ready for the still, while the virgin liquid pressed from white wine pomace will need to be fermented separately. Distilled, they make marc or grappa that can either be enjoyed in its own right or used as the base spirit for liqueurs.

Many if not most English winemakers on their own will not produce enough of this valuable resource to be worth distilling: the proportion of dry(ish) material left over after pressing ranges from 18–40 per cent per tonne of grapes, which yields anything from 4–8 litres of juice per 100kg depending on how hard the grapes were originally pressed. The most efficient winemaker, then, will be able to wring a mere seven litres of fermentable juice from the pomace of a tonne of grapes, while the least efficient will still only be left with 32 litres. After this has been watered down to about 9 per cent ABV, then distilled, then watered down again to 40 per cent ABV you would only get 4-18 70cl bottles of marc per tonne of grapes harvested which, even at £20+ per bottle, is hardly going to make much difference to your bottom line (although the leftovers or rackings from the bottling can also go into the still). However in eastern France the smaller makers, who are a byword for thrift, either send their pomace to a contract distiller or own co-operatives that run a still between them. Whichever option they choose, few

English winemakers are so profitable that they can ignore the contribution that marc can make to their viability. It is, after all, money for nothing in that the pomace at present is used only as compost or mulch: effectively, it's dumped.

So far only a handful of English and Welsh winemakers have dipped their toes tentatively into the world of spirits and liqueurs, but none of them regrets the experiment. An afternoon's reflection – especially if it is accompanied by a frosty glass of kir made with their own wine and some bought-in crème de cassis – might tempt them to dip more than just a toe.

## Cidermakers

To brewers and winemakers among those who can benefit from distilling must be added the growing army of cidermakers. Not only did they start it all, but the last 15 years has seen a huge increase in the number of small commercial cidermakers operating not only in the four traditional regions of the South-West, the West Midlands, East Anglia and the South-Eastern counties, but in Cheshire, Northamptonshire, Berkshire – even Yorkshire. In terms of raw numbers their increase has been almost as impressive as the explosion in the number of craft brewers, if far less well-documented; but thanks to the exemption from duty of cidermakers who sell less than 7,000 litres a year they are mostly far too small to consider branching out into distilling except, perhaps, as a co-operative. But for duty purposes the amount they set aside for distilling would be additional to the amount they sold, so they could make any quantity of cider they chose, sell up to 7,000 litres duty free, and distill the rest.

And there is a considerable tranche of ambitious independent cidermakers who are becoming more and more frustrated at the barriers they face in getting their product to market. Supermarkets, the continuing concentration of convenience store ownership and supply, and the gradual

## Case study – Cotswold Distillery
### www.cotswoldsdistillery.com

North Oxfordshire, it's probably safe to say, had no great tradition of whisky-making until Dan Szor decided to create one, and in the process gave a masterclass in the importance of ready access to sufficient capital.

New Yorker Dan spent 26 years as a currency trader, mostly in Paris and London, before his eureka moment hit him on a trip to Bruichladdich in May 2013. Ten years earlier he'd bought a cask to lay down and was on his annual pilgrimage to pat it and stroke it when he mentioned to manager Jim McEwan that he'd been thinking about founding a distillery of his own. Jim simply told him to get on with it and recommended him to master distiller Harry Cockburn, veteran of 15 start-ups across the globe, and suddenly the project was flying.

"I spoke to Jim on the Friday, rang Harry on the Sunday and on the Monday we were in Sweden looking at second-hand equipment," says Dan.

The speed at which events moved from then on were probably less terrifying to a City trader than they would be to the rest of us, but a mere 14 months later Dan was able to fire up his 500L Holstein gin rectifying still while his two Forsyth copper pot stills – a 2,400L wash still and a 1,600L spirit still – were only waiting to be connected to the gas before his first batch of new-make whisky dripped out of the condenser.

Luck, it must be said, played its part in the breakneck pace of developments, although it must also be said that fortune favours the brave, and much of Dan's 'luck' was a product of his energy, his business experience and acumen, and his access to some pretty substantial chunks of capital. Exactly the right premises in the form of a newly-built house and barn, empty as the result of a planning wrangle, came on the market just five miles away from Dan and wife Katia's country home. The house (built on a grant of light industrial use, hence the wrangle) was absolutely perfect for the laboratory, offices and shop; while the barn is possibly the most spacious new-wave stillhouse in the land. The pot stills also materialised by a stroke of luck. Having given up on second-hand equipment Dan and Harry resigned themselves to an indeterminate spell on Forsyth's waiting list when suddenly the phone rang – a cancellation; would they like to...? Yes they would. And yes they could.

Dan and Harry decided to source their malt from Warminster, whose boss Chris Garrett introduced them to a local farmer with 2,000 acres of organic Odyssey barley. Warminster is able to guarantee provenance by batch-malting, which means that Cotswold can genuinely proclaim its whisky to be as local to its terroir as any Scottish single malt. Then Dan heard that the Malvern Mineral Water spring had been closed three years earlier, and promptly had it reopened. So the barley and the water would be truly local, but only because Dan had made sure he had the resources to exploit unexpected opportunities. (The casks are foreigners – Bourbon barrels from Speyside Cooperage for the first fill, then sherry barrels, then US oak charred in Portugal and found by Jim Swan, to finish). Jim sadly passed away in 2017.

What will this 'grass to glass' combination of Cotswold malt and Malvern create? We'll know in 2018, when the first of the matured whisky goes into bottle. But Dan has a clue. "I love maritime peaty malts, but here we have got a definite terroir," he says. "This is a beautiful, rolling, fertile area so the notes ought to be grain and fruit with vanilla, honey, raisins, Christmas cake – a lighter whisky, blonde rather than brunette, but with plenty of depth."

closure of more and more village shops have made deep inroads into the number of genuinely independent off-licences; the 2003 Licensing Act banned the traditional but unlicensed 'farm-gate' sales; the bar franchises at agricultural shows and music festivals are now generally let to a single major operator who will tolerate no competition; and touring the circuit of farmers' markets, while it has its compensations and even its pleasures, is hugely expensive in the one resource small independents have least of – time. The number of pubs prepared to stock traditional still, dry cider is also limited and mainly both regional and seasonal, while hotel and restaurant sommeliers still almost universally regard cider as an unsophisticated rustic curiosity that doesn't belong on a drinks list. Given the example of Bertram Bulmer and Julian Temperley, therefore, and the fact that they have even less of a comfort zone than small independent brewers, it's astonishing that so few of these frustrated craft cidermakers have taken advantage of the opportunity offered by distilling. But any cidermaker dubious about its potential need only gaze on the artistry of Charles Martell of Dymock's exquisitely packaged limited-edition single-varietal pear and oak-aged plum brandies – and the prices they can command – with awe and envy, and perhaps reflect that no matter how many retailers' doors slam shut in their faces in the coming years, the door of the spirit still is always open.

## Arable farmers and fruit growers

If being already in the drinks business is a great advantage, it's by no means a precondition; indeed most of the craft distillers currently operating have come to it from a state of innocence, as it were. But having your own farm is a good start. Indeed, two of the latest entrants – Lurgashall Winery of Sussex and Bramley & Gage, originally of Devon but now based in Bristol – have actually been active for as long as

Burrow Hill, producing fine liqueurs from their own fruit and bought-in spirit (both now have their own stills). And one of the biggest of the new independent distillers, Chase of Hereford, was originally a potato farm where William Chase, the owner, decided that there was more profit in making his own crisps than selling his crop to merchants and food processors. Once the crisp business was well established it was sold on for a handsome profit, and the farm became Chase Single Estate Distillers making a variety of gins, vodkas and liqueurs based on its own produce. Unusually, Chase produces its own ethanol or neutral base spirit on its own continuous column still. This is an option any large fruit or arable farmer could benefit from. Not only does it add value to the produce, it also irons out the price fluctuations that cause so many agricultural migraines. Fruit and grain prices go up and down, but vodka, gin, and whisky prices are pretty stable.

Arable farmers seeking to add value to their barley, incidentally, have one not inconsiderable boon to thank microbrewers for. As the microbrewing sector mushroomed in the early years of this century, the perceived value of traceability and authenticity led brewers and farmers to persuade specialist maltsters such as Fawcetts of Yorkshire, Warminster of Wiltshire and Crisps of Norfolk to introduce a ground-breaking innovation. Instead of malting all the barley they bought in great homogenous batches, they worked hard to offer a facility that allowed the grain from individual farms to be processed separately. You send them your barley and they malt it, then they send it back to you. You might argue that at the end of the day it doesn't make a whole lot of difference: the purchasers at these independent maltsters are pretty expert and pretty fussy, and don't buy dodgy grain or take short cuts in the processing, so anything you source from them is going to be top-notch. But from a marketing point of view it's a huge leap forward: a brewer who can boast that their beer is brewed exclusively with malt from a particular farm has a very strong advantage in terms of provenance. And if, like Chase, you can boast that your gin and vodka are made entirely from your own produce... well! Today, posher label; tomorrow, Protected Geographical Indication (PGI) status!

## Advantages of distilling

Anything that contains sugar can be fermented and distilled, whatever its condition. Starchy grains such as wheat and maize don't even have to be malted, so long as there is enough barley malt in the mash – about 20 per cent – to produce the enzyme diastase to saccharify them. Fruit, be it soft fruit, top fruit or stone fruit, doesn't have to be uniform and unblemished if it's only going to be pressed, fermented and distilled. Roots too, especially carrots, swedes, parsnips and beet, contain bountiful amounts of fermentable sugar. And of course, if you're not striving to produce uniformly pretty fruit and veg to satisfy the supermarket buyer both your input costs (including labour) and your wastage will be significantly reduced. This is a problem for root vege-table growers in particular: half or more than half of their produce might be rejected by the supermarkets and either goes as cattle feed at £10 a tonne (compared to the £800 per tonne the supermarket chains pay) or, worse, straight to landfill. If growers either individually or in joint ventures distilled ethanol from their reject tonnage they would make considerably more than £10 a tonne – and they'd still have the pomace and pot ale to sell as animal feed or as a source of biogas.

Even if growers don't see themselves as the gin barons of the future, ethanol is a valuable product in its own right. The number of small craft distillers is set to mushroom and nearly all of them will want to buy in their ethanol, whose price is broadly increasing along with world demand. For ethanol is not only foundation of all gin, vodka and liqueurs, it's also the bio-additive that's supposed to make our motoring greener, and the minimum addition to petrol in the EU is set to rise from 5 per cent to 7 per cent by 2020. This will undoubtedly push the price up, so farmer-distillers who decide not to go into drinks production, or are left with surplus ethanol, will find a ready market for it.

## Artisan fruit growers

You don't have to be a big farmer to make a profitable business out of spirits, though. A more low-key, artisanal approach presents just as great an opportunity, especially for smaller fruit growers with little to invest either in terms of time or capital. In Charles Dickens's day Britain had a great tradition of both home-made and proprietary alcoholic cordials and liqueurs that were at bottom no more than fruit macerated in ethanol, sweetened, strained and brought down to potable strength either with wine, water or even fruit juice. Sloe gin is almost the sole survivor of this tradition in this country, but in most European countries you can buy little bottles of ethanol in supermarkets to make your own liqueurs with.

To transform your own surplus, damaged, blemished or even over-ripe fruit into a liqueur is simplicity itself (although the necessary permissions and paperwork aren't so simple, as we shall see!) and the price premium these kind of products commands will make you wonder why you ever bothered selecting and selling perfect fruit for the table in the first place. The easiest option is simply to steep your fruit in ethanol, but you can also take the process to the next level of sophistication by investing in a small still and redistilling your fruit with bought-in ethanol.

To be more sophisticated yet, you can make wine from your fruit and distill that. The equipment need not be all that expensive nor take up all that much space; and if you're too busy in the fruit-picking season itself to make your liqueur or cordial or eau-de-vie, you can pulp and freeze the fruit and come back to it in winter when you have more time. All sorts of herbs and nuts can be treated in exactly the same way to make quirky hand-crafted liqueurs that have strong impulse-purchase appeal in suitable retail environments such as country gift shops and farmers' markets, as well as online.

In fact the consumer appeal of hand-made small-batch liqueurs and eau-de vie – as with jams and chutneys – is as much down to their artisanal nature as to their quality. How they're packaged and presented and where they're bought is as important as how well they measure up against their mainstream equivalents. Quality is still vital if you want customers ever to buy a second bottle: all too often a tempting-looking pot of kitchen-made marmalade is, when you get it home from the farm shop, no better tasting than Frank Cooper's but twice the price. That, perhaps, is a story for another day; what's important for our purposes here is how to make the most of that artisanal feel, and the answer to that is simple: tourism.

## Tourism and heritage sites

More than half of Scotland's whisky distilleries have visitor centres, restaurants, cafes, shops and guided tours of varying degrees of sophistication. More and more distilleries are investing in similar facilities: the long-established Beefeater Gin distillery in Kennington, South London, opened a visitor centre back in 2014, and the Bombay Sapphire distillery in rural Hampshire will be almost as much a tourist attraction as a working factory. There are three reasons why tourists are lured to this kind of place. They like the heritage angle. They like to see traditional and authentic methods and ingredients in action. Then they like the aesthetics, especially the gleaming copper and mellow old oak. And finally, the fact that alcohol is the end-product creates an extra dimension – one of naughtiness.

Craft distilleries should never turn their backs on the tourism angle. Few of them, perhaps, could run to much more than after-hours guided tours followed by a short sampling session, especially for trade parties (but do remember: you have to have a liquor licence to sell from your premises these days!); but where a tourist attraction cannot always be bolted on to a small distillery, a small distillery might more easily be bolted on to a tourist attraction.

Until 1823 it was perfectly legal to distill for home consumption and many great houses did it, as did a number of coaching inns. The Excise Act of that year effectively (although not explicitly) banned the use of stills of less than 40 gallons' capacity, reasoning that a 40-gallon copper pot was too big and heavy for a Highland moonshiner to hide or, should the Excisemen appear, run away with. However, the Act also made it easier and cheaper to get a licence for a commercial-sized still. At this point the English country house and farm distillers simply gave up and started buying what they needed from wine merchants instead; and in fact there have been remarkably few prosecutions for moonshining in England down the years. The legal ins and outs of the situation will be explained at the appropriate stage, but HMRC seems fairly relaxed these days about licensing small rectifying stills (subject to stringent security – not a drop is to leave the premises until the duty has been paid on it), so perhaps the pre-1823 country house distilling tradition is due a revival. And a small rectifier in the old stable block would not only be an attraction in its own right, but also a powerful boost to the gift shop's bottom line!

## Licensed retailers

There is another category of established drinks businesses

## Case study – Dunnet Bay
### www.dunnetbaydistillers.co.uk

Perhaps because it's such an expensive industry to set up in, small-scale distilling hasn't attracted very many of what are termed "lifestyle entrepreneurs": that is, people who see their business as supporting the way they live rather than dictating it, and often as much an ideological construct as a commercial one. And it's not just the amount of capital required to get the thing going that dampens its appeal for entrants of this kind; it's the level of sales they have to achieve and maintain in order to justify the investment.

For Martin and Claire Murray, though, establishing the Dunnet Bay distillery near Thurso in their native Caithness has been as much a labour of love as a hard-headed business decision.

With a Master's in chemical engineering from Heriot-Watt, Martin fancied a life in distilling but at the university's careers fair found only four distillers represented, each with a single vacancy to fill. On the other hand there were jobs going begging in oil and gas and, he says: "With a student loan to pay I had to let my head rule my heart." That was in 2004. He's been in oil and gas ever since.

But in 2012 Martin, by now married to tourism and hospitality graduate Claire and with a young family to support, faced a critical decision. They were living in France, but all the while yearning for the north of Scotland, when Martin's employers asked him to relocate to Nigeria.

"We'd been thinking about our own distillery, but that was when we decided to go into it in detail," says Claire, who grew up in Dunnet where the Murrays already owned a house. "It was definitely a lifestyle choice. With a young family, we wanted a settled life and Caithness was where we wanted to be. We both grew up here and it's a truly beautiful region – not enough people know about it, and part of what we wanted to do was spread the word about it."

Not unnaturally, the Murrays' first thought was of whisky, but after considering the expense of building and equipping a full-mash distillery and the time lag before they could sell any of the product, they opted for gin instead. But this is gin with a distinctly local flavour:

"We went out with the countryside rangers and they showed us what herbs and berries grew wild and what was good to eat, and we came up with a blend of botanicals we could be confident of," says Martin. So in Dunnet Bay's Rock Rose gin you'll find ingredients such as rose root, rowanberry, blueberry and sea buckthorn.

Next they had to find a site – and as luck would have it there was a suitable vacant lot in Dunnet itself, complete with its own stream. By the end of 2013 the project was well under way, with building work about to begin on the vacant lot and a 500-litre still on order from John Dore. But how to publicise the venture? Claire had a brilliant idea. She simply sent a Christmas card to anyone she could think of who might want to order a case. More than six months before Dunnet Bay went into production a buzz had been started that ensured that the first batch, when it arrived in August 2014, was an instant sell-out. As was the second. And the third...

Which was just as well, as Martin says the total investment in buying the land, building a distillery on it, then equipping the distillery was in the region of £200,000. Some of it came from a regional enterprise grant, but the Murrays raised 70 per cent of it themselves.

A new visitor centre is planned which is due to be completed in May 2017 and there is a small gift shop open between 10–4pm.

that is slowly beginning to grasp the potential of owning its own spirits brands, and that's the licensed retail trade. The big supermarket chains, of course, have had their own labels for years, always mass-produced and mostly at the value end of the scale. Long-established independent wine merchants such as Tanners of Shrewsbury have also traditionally had their house Scotches blended for them, as have family brewers with renowned wine and spirit divisions such as Palmer's of Bridport, the much-lamented Eldridge Pope of Dorchester and Adnams of Southwold. Indeed, before the meltdown of the brewing industry that started in the 1960s it was the norm for breweries to supply their tied estates with their own exclusive 'house' brands of spirits.

But now a new trend is just beginning to emerge: craft-distilled spirit brands exclusive to upmarket restaurants and pubs. In two Cambridge restaurants, Alimentum and La Raza, they are adding even more cachet to their names by having their own gins custom-made by the bespoke specialist Cambridge Distillery; Exeter's Fat Pig chain of microbrewery and four pubs now has its own very profitable microdistillery; and in Liverpool a revered real ale pub – the Belvedere Arms in the Georgian quarter – has created its own gin, establishing a distillery on premises jointly owned with its partner in the business, Liverpool Organic Brewery. It's not the only gin sold at the Belvedere, which stocks 18, but it's a powerful draw for the pub as well as a profitable line in its own right.

## Boutique distilleries

Perhaps even more significant for the longer term has been the opening of two boutique bar-distilleries in very different but equally dynamic parts of London. The first, in Bride Lane just off Fleet Street, was the City of London Distillery in 2012. Two German-made Arnold Holstein gin stills were installed behind huge glass screens in the 'speakeasy-style retro cocktail bar' (although the last thing you would find in a real speakeasy would be any visible evidence of alcohol production) by Exigo Brewing & Distilling of Leicester, which two years later did much the same thing at the Bow Wharf Bar, a Victorian former glue-factory off Grove Road in Globe Town, East London.

Now, slowly but surely, other equally upmarket independent pubs and pub chains, boutique hotels and Michelin-starred restaurants are beginning to follow suit and install distilleries of their own.

## None of the above...

The drive and vision required of a successful entrepreneur are not limited to people who already have, in one way or another, a foot in the door. Most of the players in the craft distilling revival, in fact, had no previous track-record in the industry. Like all entrepreneurs, they set out with an idea and access to enough capital to assemble the nuts and bolts of the business. Since then it has been largely a question of intelligent decision-making, utter commitment and hard work – especially in the marketing: Sion Edwards and Tom Warner of Warner Edwards attended more than 60 farmers' markets, trade shows and other events in their first full year of operation. But that's life for pretty much any entrepreneur in pretty much any enterprise. If you have the energy and ambition to succeed, exploit market opportunities, and a strong sense that there's something special – something romantic, even – about distilling, then the class of person most qualified to build a strong, solid business in spirits is a class of one: you.

# 02

# Meet the Family

Having decided that diversification into spirits and liqueurs is right for your business – or even that you want to start up from scratch – it's worth taking some time to explore not just their commercial potential but also which product or products are most appropriate for you. This, of course, will depend on where your business is now and where you want it to be in a few years' time; but whatever your ambition you will find that there's a product to match it... and it might not be the obvious one.

## EU spirit classifications

The gamut of spirits embraces far more than the mainstream of whisky, brandy, gin, rum and vodka, and even these are capable of almost infinite variation. In recent years established distillers have been creating new and surprising expressions for their traditional mainstays, but that's only the beginning: there's a whole world of liqueurs, cordials, aperitifs, digestifs and macerations too, each with its own niche from high-flying global brand to craft-made regional delicacy. The European Parliament's 2008 Spirit Drinks Regulation (110/2008, to give it its jargon name) is essentially a round-up of all the relevant legislation current in the member states. It lists 46 categories of spirits and liqueurs produced in the EU from the obvious ones like whisky, gin, vodka, brandy and rum to local specialities such as spritglögg, nocino and guignolet; and somewhere out there, there are people making liqueurs out of mulberry, bilberry, cloudberry, arctic bramble, lingonberry, sea buckthorn, and gentian.

Britain used to have a similar tradition of the distillation or infusion in spirits of fruits, herbs, and spices to make liqueurs, cordials, medicines, and cosmetics – Peter Jonas's *The Distiller's Guide* (1818) lists such ingredients as wormwood, cinnamon, lavender, cardamom, caraway, scurvy-grass, ambergris and musk among many, many others. Then in 1823 the Excise Act killed off the practice of making home-distilled drinks when it stipulated a minimum still capacity of 40 gallons for all except apothecaries and perfumiers. But the amazing range of possibilities still exists, and creates an opportunity for innovation – which consumers go wild for, as we know from recent history. Take the brewing industry: compare the supermarket shelves of today with their wheat beers, IPAs, golden ales, cappucino stouts, chocolate porters, raspberry lambics and heaven knows what else with those of only 20 years ago when the choice was Guinness, Newcastle Brown, cheap canned bitter or cheap canned lager. Over an admittedly longer period we have seen the same phenomenon in the wine trade, too: once it was either staid, stuffy French with its impenetrable labels; cheap and cheerful Spanish and Italian; or faintly alcoholic sugar-water from Germany. Now – well!

If the spirits industry has been generally slower to innovate, there have been good reasons. It became a global business dominated by multinational corporations long before the brewing industry did, with the inevitable difficulties in focusing on individual markets. And brand values have been more concerned with heritage and authenticity than with modernity and excitement. Given the traditional core demographic – middle-aged, middle-class and at least well-off if not actually rich – this is hardly surprising.

But for some time now the demographic has been changing. The progressive reduction in the duty differential between beer and spirits has made spirits more accessible to the less well-off; and the presence of more and more women, not in the main beer-drinkers, in the market has seen the onward march of vodka and, latterly, more exotic spirits, especially tequila. New styles of spirits, new brands of spirits, even new ways of drinking spirits provoked a renewed attention to marketing and a more dynamic spirit of innovation. At first this applied mainly to standard brands priced to suit mainstream markets, but more recently we have seen the same phenomenon in the premium sector as well. Brand extensions such as Snow Grouse and Black Grouse, eye-catching vatted malts such as Monkey Shoulder whose branding and design is a challenge to American whiskeys... these were considered daring when they first arrived, but are pretty much old hat now.

## Gin

Gin has a fascinating history. Originally a Dutch invention, it's emphatically not the spirit that English troops so gleefully encountered in the Netherlands during Queen Elizabeth I's war against Spain, and which gave us the expression "Dutch courage". That, as we shall discover, was grape brandy.

Gin was supposedly invented and was certainly popularised by one Dr Sylvius as a medicinal tincture rather than a beverage. The juniper berries which give it its name were (and are) prescribed by herbalists for ailments of the digestive tract from heartburn to urinary dysfunction as well as gout, arthritis and other problems with the joints. (A close cousin is the Scandinavian caraway-infused akvavit, caraway claiming much the same medicinal properties as juniper.) From the mid-16th century onwards Dutch doctors infused juniper and other curatives in exactly the same malt spirit that, in Scotland and Ireland, would go on to become whisky and which was called "korenwijn" in Dutch. A large population and a distinct shortage of dry land, though, meant that grain was in short supply and korenwijn was too expensive to be sold as a beverage: hence brandewijn (see below). Gin or genever only really took off once the great programme of land reclamation in the early 17th century had eased the grain shortage.

## English gin distilling

Then in 1688 the Dutch ruler, William of Orange, also became King of England and banned the import of brandy in pursuance of his perpetual war with France. Gin distilling quickly became a huge industry in England, with vast malt distilleries in London processing intensively-farmed East Anglian barley and selling on the spirit to a huge network of small independent rectifiers. In the late 18th century the malt distillers produced more wash than the city's brewers made beer, while at the height of the "gin fever" of the same period almost every grocer in London was also a rectifier. Gin finally dropped the bad name (or names: Blue Devil, Mother's Ruin, and so on) that it had picked up in the 18th century in the days of the Raj, when it had quinine added to it as an anti-malarial, and in the hedonistic 1920s and '30s when it became the base spirit in a myriad cocktails. By the 1950s it was as thoroughly respectable as Scotch.

But if anyone had predicted even five years ago that it would ever shake off its golf-club image and become sexy again...! And yet it has. Indeed, as we have seen, it has been the driving force behind the craft distilling boom's latest growth spurt. But what exactly is gin? Well, all consumers know (or should do) that's it's a clear spirit that tastes mainly of juniper. But 110/2008 recognises three qualities of gin. Basic gin need be no more than neutral spirit flavoured with either natural or "nature-identical" juniper and other botanicals; to qualify as distilled gin the flavourings must be added by redistillation; and finally all the botanicals in the top-quality London gin must be natural. Gin has to be sold at a minimum of 37.5% ABV; but there is a fourth category, "juniper spirit", which can be sold at a minimum of 30% ABV. The neutral spirit can be distilled from any fermented liquor – Chase even makes it from cider – but only in oude genever (oude meaning old-fashioned rather than aged) will you find more than a token percentage of distilled pure malt liquor. (Dutch and Flemish genevers have separate EC definitions.) To be classified as dry, distilled or London gin may contain no more than 0.1g of sugar per litre of the final product.

## Botanicals

But back to the botanicals, which are after all what makes gin gin. The expression is shorthand for the grist of herbs, spices, fruits and flowers either thrown directly into the rectifying still or, for a little more subtlety, hung in its neck in a mesh bag to surrender their volatiles and aromatics gently to the ascending spirit vapour. Often the botanicals are steeped in hot spirit for several hours before the addition to burst the juniper berries' skins and improve the extraction of aromatics.

With the caveat that juniper must be the predominant flavour, almost any organic substance can be used. Some of the more traditional ones – liquorice root, cassia bark, orris root, angelica – come straight out of medieval herbals. Others – zest of bitter oranges, lemon zest, cinnamon, cardamom seed, anise, saffron, coriander, nutmeg – are more familiar from the medieval cookbook. In recent times fairly strong or at any rate highly distinctive flavourings – elderflower, rose petals, cucumber, birch sap – have been introduced as pleasing novelties; and although of course they are not supposed to drown out the taste of juniper, there are now so many premium gins on the market that the need to stand out from the crowd is bound to tempt some blenders to stretch the definitions somewhat: one reviewer described a particular craft gin as tasting like Ribena.

Sourcing the huge range of botanicals you will want to try out might seem a little overwhelming, but is not actually a problem: companies such as Beacon Supplies and Cotswold Ingredients have got it covered, so you don't have to search the highways and byways and the woods and meadows for obscure herbs. But you can if you want to; you might even regard it as all part of the fun or, more likely, the mark of a truly local artisan. In fact Bruichladdich on Islay, which makes its own Botany gin, does exactly that, gathering spearmint, applemint, thistle, birch, gorse flowers, hawthorn blossom, thyme, sage, meadowsweet, clovers both red and white and heaven knows what else from the countryside around the distillery to create a rather extravagant mélange of 22 botanicals (10–12 is more usual).

## Ethanol suppliers

And then there's all that neutral spirit. Very few craft gin producers actually distill their own base spirit: it's a huge undertaking. There is, though, a looming world shortage of ethanol as more and more countries increase the amount that must be added to petrol. It is still a good deal cheaper to buy it in and virtually all of the new wave British gin distillers buy theirs from suppliers such as Alcohols Ltd of Bishop's Stortford, a family firm that operates the fascinating Langley Green distillery, a Victorian former brewery in central Birmingham, or from Hayman Speciality Products, a branch of Hayman Ltd of Witham, Essex, also known for its Old Tom gin. Others import theirs from either of the two huge grain distilleries at Calais, or even from Pakistan. But if the ethanol shortage worsens a spirit still might turn out to be a good investment (especially if you can sell any surplus to Shell!).

# Vodka

Vodka is one of the family of clear grain-based spirits that emerged pretty much all over Northern Europe before the 16th century. Its production is recorded in Sweden, Poland and Lithuania as well as Russia, although Soviet historians have attempted to make the case that it was first distilled

## Case study – Penderyn
### www.welsh-whisky.co.uk

Hard to think of a company that's only as old as the century as a veteran, but in the context of craft distilling, that's exactly what Penderyn is.

Wales's first functioning whisky distillery for over a century, Penderyn stands in the village of the same name between the Rhondda and the Brecon Beacons. It has a somewhat melancholy prehistory: much of the original equipment, including the specially-designed Faraday still, came from a failed venture that, had it lived, would have pioneered craft distilling by a decade.

The Welsh Whisky Company, headed by Welsh Development Agency chief economist Brian Morgan, had raised nearly £1,000,000 in equity, debt and grants. It looked sound, but the early years were a struggle. Its cask club and white spirits failed to find acceptance; cash flow was more of a trickle; the capital steadily disappeared; and by the time the first real Welsh whisky for over a century was ready to bottle, the company needed £1,000,000 of fresh capital from a new investor, Nigel Short, just to survive.

With new finance came new CEO Stephen Davies. His first priority was to gain distribution throughout the UK, generating the cash to increase production and lay down stocks for export. At the time Penderyn was sending only 10–15 per cent of its output abroad on a case-by-case basis.

Success at home, including the growing popularity of the company's own gin, held back the export drive, eating into the mature stocks that were being slowly built up. By 2012 export sales had just topped 20 per cent of output, although in volume terms they had been increasing by 17 per cent year-on-year.

Those were years of cautious expansion while Penderyn geared up for a serious attempt on selected markets. "We were a small company with limited stocks, and there was no point rushing out and spending money in markets we couldn't service," says Mr Davies. A second Faraday still was installed along with two conventional pot stills that together would more than double capacity; after that a mash tun and fermenters were added (previously the wash had come from Brains of Cardiff).

"With an unfamiliar product like Welsh whisky we had to be cautious and build slowly," says Mr Davies. "We met some agents through personal introductions and others at events like Whisky Live. And yes, we have had one or two disappointments where we had to change distributors because they were either too large or too small; but we did so very reluctantly because what you need is a long-term relationship. It takes time to build a brand:

At time of writing, Penderyn had started building its presence in Far Eastern markets including Taiwan, China, Japan and Australia; but Mr Davies sees the US as key to longer-term growth. One of many expressions of Penderyn designed unashamedly to appeal to the US market, Independence, trades on the fact that 11 of the signatories of the Declaration of Independence were of Welsh extraction.

Ironically, though, just as the export strategy seems to be taking off, along comes yet more success in the home market. The whisky is among the most widely-distributed new-wave spirit brands in Britain; the on-site visitor centre and shop are among the most popular attractions in the Principality, attracting 40,000 visitors in 2016; and in summer 2016 the company won planning permission to build a second distillery as part of the redevelopment of Swansea's historic Hafod Morfa Copperworks.

in the Principality of Moscow as early as the 14th century when agricultural advances created a grain surplus. Vodka is traditionally triple-distilled, originally perhaps because either the mixture or the strains of cereals used in the wash didn't ferment well (a fault that, coincidentally, played an important part in the development of lager), and the wash was therefore low in alcohol and contained an unacceptable level of fusel oils and other impurities. Whether it's the extra run through the still or the more than usually ruthless discarding of heads and tails followed by filtration through activated charcoal that does the trick, vodka's most distinctive attribute has always been its purity. The rigorous processing has also allowed distillers to use almost any fermentable material in the wash: all sorts of grain, potatoes, grapes and other fruit, even pure sugar.

The resurgence of gin owes an awful lot to the intense marketing activity put behind vodka by companies large and small from the 1980s onwards. The only thing anybody knew about vodka before then was that James Bond drank it and that it didn't leave you with much of a hangover. Oh, and that Vladivar came from Varrington. Then imported brands with real provenance – Stolichnaya from Russia, Wyborowa with its flavoured variants from Poland, Finlandia (from guess where), Absolut from Sweden – came along and injected excitement into a younger market that craved authenticity, exoticism and novelty. Many others have followed – Black Death, Grey Goose, Russian Standard – to keep the market bubbling.

## Vodka and purity

It's often been said, and quite unfairly, that vodka's popularity among younger drinkers is down to its lack of character. It's true that good vodka is highly refined – indeed, it's characterised in the European regulations as being "distilled and/or rectified so that the organoleptic characteristics of the raw materials used and the by-products formed in fermentation are selectively reduced." Subtle is not the same as bland, though; and the smoothness of a really top-quality vodka could almost be described as a flavour component in its own right. But what has really attracted the drinkers is vodka's versatility as a platform for any number of combinations – some younger drinkers (probably too young) even dissolve Skittles in it!

Vodka is making quite a splash on the craft distilling scene, partly as a cocktail base in trendy bars but not least because it lends itself to unusual and eyecatching flavours such as Adnams Toffee Vodka and Chase's Marmalade Vodka. And these aren't just gimmicks: the Poles in particular have a long and respectable tradition of flavouring their vodkas with all sorts of substances – bison grass springs to mind – and Regulation 110/2008 has a separate heading for flavoured vodkas.

## Whisky

Whisky distilling is so shrouded in myth and mystery that folk south of the border have had a blind spot about it for generations. Making gin and vodka in Scotland – fine. Making whisky in England or Wales – it seems wrong somehow. Whisky comes from glens, period. Actually, though, whisky fuelled the second spurt of the craft distilling revival. Inspired by the appearance of new artisan distilleries in Scotland – Isle of Arran, Speyside, Kilchoman, Daftmill, Loch Ewe – came the arrival down south of Penderyn in Wales, St George's in Norfolk, Hicks & Healey in Cornwall and Adnams in Suffolk and, in the next wave, the London Distillery Company that is intent on making the first malt whisky in London for well over 100 years. It's true, though, that making whisky is a more involved business than making gin or vodka.

## Ale distilling and the role of oak

It wasn't ever thus, for although whisky appears to be almost the opposite of gin in character, the two have exactly the same origin. Late medieval apothecaries routinely extracted the active constituents of herbs and other substances – especially water-insoluble alkaloids such as quinine – by infusion in the spirits they produced on their bench-top retorts and alembics. At some point they switched from distilling wine, which was expensive, to distilling ale, which was cheap. The first British record of this switch comes from Scotland in 1494, although it may have occurred much earlier. In the early 16th century somebody discovered that this medicine, taken well-watered, was more than merely efficacious – it was also bloomin' delicious.

In the mid-16th century the distillation of unhopped ale became an economic staple of small farmers in Scotland and Ireland: it gave them a way of storing the surplus barley of good years to sell at a premium in lean ones; and it was the long storage in oak barrels that defined whisky not as a raw new spirit that needed to be flavoured to make it potable but as a rich, rounded and mellow luxury, infused with tannin and vanillin from the oak and with its aldehydes, tannins and methyls broken down by time, and one that continued to improve both in quality and value with keeping.

## Whisky all over the world

Still, it was only in the 19th century that whisky began its career of global conquest. Celts exiled by the Highland clearances and the Irish potato famine exported the art of whisky distilling to North America; the adoption of the continuous still made possible the mass-production of affordable and consistent blends; and finally the phylloxera epidemic that almost wiped out viticulture in France in the 1860s and '70s created a world shortage of brandy and a vacuum that Scottish whisky merchants were able to fill. Today whisky is made all over the world – not just Scotland, Ireland and North America, but India, Japan, Pakistan, Tasmania, New Zealand, the Czech Republic, Spain, Belgium, France, even England and Wales – but surprisingly little of it is distilled from the pure malt liquor that gave birth to it. The giant column stills that make grain whisky for blending will devour almost any kind of cereal – American whiskies are made of rye and maize, and one patriotic Breton distiller has bravely made whisky from the blé noir or buckwheat that is a speciality of the region but isn't even a cereal. (And which doesn't make very palatable whisky!)

Craft distillers interested in whisky probably won't want to make grain spirit on giant columns, though, or experiment with grains other than the finest malting barley and perhaps rye (but certainly not blé noir!). Batch-distilled pure malt whisky is what they're after, and they prefer to carry out the whole process themselves; and that's why whisky-making is a far more involved business than making gin. It starts with brewing the wash – that is, making a strong unhopped all-malt liquor of around 8–9% ABV. This goes into the still for a cleansing run that sorts out the worst of the aldehydes, fusel oil, methyl compounds and all the other bad stuff (some of which is kept back to be redistilled). A second run through the still completes the process (although some makers give the spirit a third run too, for good measure); and the "new make" is filled in wooden barrels (usually, but not necessarily, oak) with a maximum capacity of 700 litres for at least three years. Not all of the new-wave whisky distillers make their own wash: Healey & Hicks gets its wash from St Austell Brewery, and Penderyn until recently got its from Brains; but there's certainly no question of buying in neutral alcohol as gin distillers can. Control over the whole process, or as much as is practical, is the thing. Oh – and waiting for at least three years before you get so much as a penny of your investment back

## Whisky or whiskey?

Finally, a word on the variant spellings. "Whisky" has, over the years, come to denote Scotch and its descendants in Canada, India and elsewhere, while Ireland and the US have "whiskey". The two words are identical in every respect save the interpolated "e" and do not – or did not originally – describe different processes or raw materials. Orthography in the 18th century was a chancy business, and spellings were far from standard, which is why today we still have variants such as sew and sow, cider and cyder, and whisky and whiskey. Regulation 110/2008 makes no distinction between the two; nor, for that matter, does it make a distinction between malt whisky produced on a pot still and grain whisky produced on a column still – but that's a story for another day.

# Brandy

If you've ever wondered why a spirit derived from wine has a Dutch name – it's a contraction of brandewijn or 'burnt wine' – it's because those industrious Dutch invented not just gin but brandy too. Well, that's not quite true: they invented the brandy industry. Eau-de-vie had been made in Western France and exported since the early 16th century, but in such small quantities that it can only have been as feedstock for apothecaries in Northern European countries where wine was too expensive to be used for distilling: one docket from 1549 records the export of just four barrels.

The 16th century Dutch were already good customers for paper from the heavily-forested Cognac region but got their wines from Spain and Burgundy, these being other components of the Hapsburg patrimony of which the Netherlands formed a part. Once the Dutch rebelled in 1572 these sources of wine were cut off, so they started importing from the Charente instead. Charentais wines, though, were so acidic that they were really only suitable for distilling, so that's what the Dutch did with them. In time the Charentais wine merchants started putting their existing skills to good use and distilling their wines themselves, often using stills provided by their Dutch customers. In the meantime, though, the Dutch had discovered, just as the Scottish did, the wonders wrought by the interaction of spirit and oak. Time spent in barrels – in transit, and in warehouses awaiting sale – transformed the clear eau-de-vie into what we would recognise as brandy; once the French distillers had learnt the same trick, oak-aged brandy took the western world by storm. Oak ageing is still part of the EC Regulation's requirement for brandy today, although the stipulated period is not as long as that for whisky.

## Marc and grappa

Brandy might not be of as much interest to would-be distillers in Britain as gin and whisky: few English and Welsh vineyards produce the volumes that would be required to yield a quantity of spirit that would repay the capital investment required to produce it, although as we have seen Ludlow distills both on its own account and for neighbouring vineyards. Brandy's youthful sibling marc, though, might well be a more generally viable proposition. Common in Italy – grappa is a form of marc – and the eastern winemaking regions of France, it's the distillate of the residue contained in the pulp left over after winemaking. In the case of red wine, which gets it colour from macerating the skins, the lees may already have been fermented and the juice extracted from them can go straight to the still; white wine lees will have to be separately fermented before distillation. Marc can be drunk on its own, but it also makes an excellent base spirit for fruit eau-de-vie and liqueurs, either rectified or simply infused. It's certainly a good use for a by-product that otherwise ends up as animal feed! And if a single vineyard doesn't generate enough lees to be worth distilling, there's absolutely no reason why a number shouldn't get together and do it as a collective.

## Fruit brandies

The craft distilling revival was accompanied, perhaps appropriately, by a right old hoo-hah that pitted implacable Brussels bureaucrats against two true-blue British bulldogs who wouldn't take "non" for an answer. And as you might expect of such a Herculean contest, it was all over a single word. The late Bertram Bulmer of Bulmers and Julian Temperley of Burrow Hill Cider both wanted to make brandy out of their cider that they, perhaps not unreasonably, both wanted to call cider brandy. But, protested Brussels, there can be no such thing as cider brandy because brandy is made out of grapes. There could be apple or cider spirit, but not cider brandy. Both Bulmer and Temperley, though, thought "cider spirit" an unmarketable name and fought their corners. Bulmer, with his high-level connections, was allowed a temporary derogation for King Offa, that has now expired; Temperley found a loophole which bizarrely allows his Somerset Royal the designation cider brandy as a regional speciality.

Squabbles over semantics aside, Regulation 110/2008 recognises several categories of fruit spirit or spirit-based fruit drink (that's liqueur to you and me), all of which are likely to be of interest to the British would-be distiller or indeed to any fruit-grower with a glut surplus or a truckload of cull that would be better turned into money than slurry.

## Eau-de-vie

'Fruit spirit' is the unlovely but official designation of what you and I would recognise as the best of the eau-de-vie de fruits from Alsace, i.e. those derived exclusively from fruits, berries or vegetables with a high enough sugar content to ferment to an alcoholic strength sufficient for distillation. This class doesn't just consist of Mirabelle or Poire Williams, though: slivovitz, barack, pálinka and their cousins, being made mainly from stone fruit, come under the same heading. Cider spirit and perry spirit (or apple brandy and pear brandy) have their own heading but almost identical regulations, and of course include Calvados and its Breton equivalent, lambig. (Oh, and Somerset Royal Cider Brandy.) Fruits whose natural sugar content is too low to be fermented into a liquor suitable for distillation can still be turned into full-strength spirit (i.e. bottled at 37.5% ABV or above) by maceration in neutral spirit and redistillation.

# Rum

The etymology of the word "rum" is unclear – it is most commonly supposed to be a contraction of the word "rumbullion", which is Tudor English for rocket-fuel. It was first distilled, like tequila, by Spanish conquistadors who failed to establish grapevines in South America and the Caribbean, and came to the world's attention in 1655 when Cromwell's fleet accidentally captured Jamaica (it had been sent to capture somewhere else entirely but failed, and seized the less well-defended Jamaica as a consolation prize – thereby, incidentally, founding the British Empire). Sugar planting rapidly spread throughout the British West Indies and mainland colonies, and since the refining process was (and is) unusually inefficient, there was plenty of sticky sweet molasses left over to be turned into rum.

There's no reason why the British craft distiller shouldn't set his or her hand to making rum – there are plenty of bulk suppliers of molasses in the food industry, two in the city of Hull alone. Of course the Cubans and Jamaicans and Australians and Mauritians are making a pretty good job of it already, so you might well ask yourself whether you could do better. The proprietors of the Dark Matters distillery in Banchory, Scotland, have asked themselves precisely that question and come up with the answer: "Yes".

## Other spirits

It must by now be clear that the world is very nearly your oyster. Given the right equipment you can distill virtually any fermented liquor that comes to hand and flavour or compound it with any fruit, nut, herb or spice that springs to mind; the only limit is the breadth of your imagination. And a modicum of common sense, of course. It would be a pretty bold entrepreneur who managed to convince himself or herself that there was a market for British-made arrack, perhaps; arrack being the spirit derived from distilling toddy, which is itself fermented palm or coconut sap. Palm sap might be a bit hard to get hold of over here, as might the agave cactus you would need if you decided to make tequila or mezcal. However there is one craft distiller – Black Cow of Beaminster in Dorset – who ferments the sugar-rich whey left over from his cheesemaking into kumiss, then distills the kumiss into Mongolian-style arak. But as only a select few know what Mongolian-style arak is – and as there is no such EU classification – he calls it vodka. And why not?

## Liqueurs

Liqueurs of various sorts together form one of the most diverse categories of spirit drinks, an indicator of the survival of craft distilling traditions in many of the less urbanised corners of the EU. What most (but not all) liqueurs have in common is that they consist of a base spirit – any form of spirits – of any strength down to a minimum of 15% ABV.

They are, in theory at least, fairly simple to make. For many if not most producers, the tricky business of installing and operating a spirit still is not part of the equation: their skill or art lies in the blending. Few of them need to make their own base spirit any more than a chef needs to rear and slaughter his own cattle. In the UK, the mixing of spirits with anything other than water is an act of compounding, for which a compounder's licence is required (and also a rectifier's licence if the flavouring is done using a still).

## Macerated liqueurs

Walk down the appropriate aisle of any supermarket and it will become apparent that the British – or the English and Welsh, at least – have no tradition of producing liqueurs other than sloe gin. It was not ever thus. In the 18th and 19th centuries very sweet macerated fruit liqueurs just like sloe gin, both home-made and proprietary, were enormously popular and tremendously varied. The base spirit was generally grain; among them native fruits currants (red, white and black), elderberries, rhubarb and damsons were common flavourings; and "medicinal" macerations included native herbs such as angelica, lovage and mint and exotic spices such as cassia, cloves, ginger and cardamom. Shrub, first recorded in the 1740s and a pub commonplace as a mixer for rum or brandy until the late 1800s, was itself composed of rum or brandy blended 2:1 with orange and sometimes lemon juice, and with an awful lot of sugar thrown in. A home-made alternative was to infuse orange and lemon zest in heavily-sweetened rum for a week or two, then water down the result.

## Compounded liqueurs

Cherries provided English blenders with one of the most distinctive of native ingredients, especially in Kent where they were principally grown. A cherry brandy might be a straightforward infusion of cherry pulp in gin with a few (but not too many!) cracked kernels left in for taste, and

49

## Case study – Ludlow
### www.ludlowvineyard.co.uk

The idea of installing a distillery came to Mike Hardingham of Ludlow Vineyard in Shropshire's Clee Hills when he sampled some 'very impressive' brandy from Moor Lynch Vineyard in Devon. Being a Calvados lover, though, he planned to major in producing apple brandy from his own cider, only distilling wine when his grape harvest was low on quality or overgenerous in quantity.

It turned out to be a long process. Stage one was to research the distillation process and equipment required, which was not all that onerous; stage two was to find out what might be required to get a licence from HMRC.

"To specify the plant, we had to get a rough idea of what kind of still we could afford," says Mike. "There are Scottish companies who will build a still to any specification, but we found it would be much cheaper to buy off the shelf from Germany, where small craft stills are produced in large numbers.

"We investigated Holstein, Christian Karl, Mueller and Kothe: in the end we settled on Kothe because the chief distiller, Dr Hagmann, spoke excellent English!"

Mike spent two days at Kothe working on the distillery design and getting some hands-on tuition, returning home having placed an order for a 200-litre pot still and a four-plate refining column. Next came the application to HMRC first for a Distillation Licence – relatively simple, thought Mike, and then for the more complicated Approval of Plant & Process.

"Writing the proposal required careful consideration of what we thought might sway HMRC into giving us a licence," he says. "And while looking into the issues we bought three barrels of English brandy dating from 1991 and 1992 from Wooton Vineyard – only to discover that we needed a licence from HMRC simply to own duty-suspended goods!"

The discovery actually proved quite useful as it enabled Mike to strike up a relationship with HMRC's Birmingham office. With their guidance, he decided there were five areas where he needed to be especially convincing:

1. That he was scrupulously honest and could be trusted not to fiddle the returns.

2. That he understood how hard-pressed and overworked HMRC staff were.

3. That he had a plausible business case for the distillery.

4. That there was a local demand for the products he had in mind.

5. That he was sufficiently accomplished technically.

"It helped that over several decades of dealing with HMRC as VAT-registered traders Ludlow had never blotted its copybook; so we started from a position of being able to talk to HMRC as friends rather than foes," he says.

The whole process took a year, of which Mike reckons he spent a total of three months on research, writing proposals, working out business models, having meetings with HMRC and so on. Once approval had been granted, it took another month to buy the distillery, modify the building in which it would be sited and install it. The distillery cost some £50,000 to set up: £20,000 for the 200-litre pot still, the rest for installation, drainage and ancillary equipment. It seems a lot, but, says Mike: "For most vineyards, making a small amount of brandy – a barrel every two or three years, say – looks economically very attractive if they can spare enough grapes."

A barrel of brandy takes about two tonnes of grapes that need to be pressed, chaptalised, fermented "in a rough and ready fashion" to 12% ABV, distilled, then matured for one to two years. "We normally ferment at low temperatures, but for distillation it can be fairly fast by normal winemaking standards," says Mike. "When fermentation has finished we distil sooner rather than later, without any racking."

Distillation generates spirit at about 85% ABV, reduced to 60% before going into either new American oak or second-hand Cognac barrels for at least six months.

"The grapes can be up to 20 per cent acid and low in sugar, which is ideal for a poor year," says Mike. "It's also ideal when grapes are plentiful and all the stainless steel tanks are full. Liquor for distillation doesn't need the same high standards required to make really good wine – a polythene IBC will do provided the wine is distilled soon after fermentation has finished."

Distillation is also a good way of turning disappointing wine into a highly marketable product: "Poor wine can make good brandy," says Mike.

A barrel will produce around 300 litres of brandy that Mike finds is best filled into 20cl and 35cl bottles. "Small sizes are popular with the typical customer, who will generally be prepared to pay at least £12.50 and £20 for these sizes," he says. "We know of some vineyards selling their brandy at over £25 a half-bottle!" Ludlow, he says, has no trouble selling one small bottle of brandy for every 10-15 bottles of wine.

The costs of turning two tonnes of grapes into brandy include fermentation, distillation, barrel maturation, bottling and duty. Pressing and fermentation will cost around £1,500. The 20 hours of distilling time at £5 for fuel, £20 for the distiller and £25 to run the equipment, amounts to another £1,000. The price of the barrel and the cost of six months maturation is £500. The barrel will yield around 300 litres of 40% ABV brandy, which costs £1,000 to bottle and attracts duty of around £3,500. The brandy will therefore have cost a total of £7,500 plus VAT. For this outlay the vineyard will have duty-paid bottles with a shelf price of around £18,000. The same two tonnes of grapes would take about the same amount of money to turn into 1,800 duty-paid bottles with a shelf-price of (you've guessed it) about £18,000. So brandy is not more profitable than wine – but on the other hand, the grapes that go to make it would be no good for anything else.

There is, however, a flaw in the maths. "A distillery is enormous fun and can add to the attraction of the vineyard for visitors," says Mike. "To recoup an investment of £50,000, though, you need to make a lot of brandy. Most vineyards will struggle to sell more than a barrel a year, so if you install your own distillery you need either to distil other liquors as well, or distil for other vineyards." And that's exactly what Mike has done, producing grappa and other spirits for neighbouring winemakers, pear, damson and greengage eau-de-vie under his own label, and a range of liqueurs including apple and elderflower, blackberry and apple, damson and juniper, and rhubarb and ginger all based on his own neutral spirit and his own fruit syrups.

plenty of syrup. This was probably the cherry cordial the Pickwickians were regaled with at Manor Farm after their long wintry trudge. But at the Crown at Sarre near Ramsgate the Huguenot landlord was reputed to distill his own, not perhaps from scratch, but compounding the cherries with a base spirit in a small still to produce a proper eau-de-vie de fruit rather than a simple maceration and thereby earning the pub the nickname it still has, the Cherry Brandy House. Perhaps the cherry brandy at Sarre was made in the same way as the cherry liqueur described by Regulation 110/2008 as using only cherry distillate for its base spirit and, with a minimum sugar content of 70g per litre, being drier than all other liqueurs whose minimum sugar content is 100g per litre (80g per litre for gentian, though).

Cherries also give us another aristocrat of the liqueur world, the strong and sweet maraschino, properly a compounded distillate of maraschino cherries although more usually a maceration in neutral spirit. Maraschino has a minimum sugar content of 250g per litre, so it's pretty sticky stuff, and a minimum strength of 24% ABV, so it can creep up on you. Sweeter still is crème de cassis, the blackcurrant infusion that makes kir what it is. It has a whopping 400g of sugar per litre minimum, although a minimum ABV of only 15 per cent; its cousin, crème de mûr, is the blackberry equivalent and has a more subtle flavour.

## Nut-based liqueurs

Finally, spare a thought for nuts. Nocino or noisette is produced by the maceration and/or distillation of whole green walnuts and is stronger than other liqueurs with a minimum ABV of 30%. The other nut-derived liqueurs – Amaretto, flavoured with almonds; Frangelico, Amaretto's hazelnut equivalent; and the French crème de châtaigne, or chestnut liqueur, which is also made in Spain and Italy – are subject to the normal regulations.

## What's your poison?

There is one particularly significant difference between the microbrewing boom and the craft distilling revival. The pioneering microbrewers were trying to get back something they believed the country had lost: wholesome, tasty and traditional cask beers brewed by people who cared not only about quality but about heritage too. Early microbrewers rediscovered several lost styles of beer, especially at the darker end of the spectrum, but it was a long time before more forward-thinking microbrewers struck out and really started innovating.

Craft distilling has a completely different driving force. In truth it isn't really a "revival" at all, although the term is too handy to discard. But small-scale distilling died out in England and Wales very nearly two centuries ago, so today's craft distillers are almost starting from scratch. Although they share what might be considered "retro" values in terms of quality and authenticity, they are not judged – and do not judge themselves – by a narrow adherence to tradition. There is, after all, not much of a tradition to adhere to. In that sense, then, the craft distiller is freer and less bound by the past than the microbrewer. So if you want to have a go at making mezcal in Manchester or pisco in Peterborough, nothing is stopping you.

Then there is the question of customer expectation. Craft distillers are a very diverse group, if indeed they can be called a group at all. The only thing they have in common is that their products are expensive. A craft-distilled gin is in the same price bracket as a single malt whisky. And the only thing that craft distillers' customers have in common is that they can afford it. But who are the customers? Are they cosmopolitan plutocrats with one foot in the City and the other in Dubai? Are they crusty old gents who might even still on occasion wear a cravat? Are they *Guardian*-reading Boden catalogue foodies who put a premium on localism and authenticity? Or are they edgy, funky hipsters whose expectations are only satisfied by the unexpected? This is a consideration that will affect not only your marketing but your choice of what to fill your spirit still with in the first place.

Well, up to a point, Lord Copper. Pioneers tend to be very confident people with an unshakeable belief both in what they're doing and how they do it. One cannot imagine Bertram Bulmer or Julian Temperley setting much store by focus groups. The success of avant-garde entrepreneurs is very often down to a faith that in the end justifies itself. Certainly in the early stages of any movement there are enough niches of unsatisfied demand – or just plain consumer curiosity – to create sufficient sales to render a modest number of small-to-medium businesses adequately profitable. Things get tougher further down the line as more and more newcomers compete for retail space that never seems to expand quite quickly enough. At that point the right product – and the right quality – becomes critical. And at that point, too, innovation starts to crack open new markets: not just innovation in products, but in ways of marketing them. Some rectifiers are already producing seasonal botanicals, so – a nutmeg, ginger, cinnamon and clove vodka cream liqueur for Christmas, anyone? One day, no doubt; one day...

# THE MICROBREWERS' HANDBOOK

## By Ted Bruning

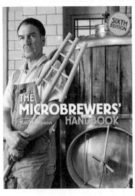

*"Indispensable if you are tempted to bolt together mash tun, copper and fermenters"*
Roger Protz

*"If you are considering creating your own brewery, whatever your motivation, you should buy and read this book as your first step"*
Hopmaltbrew.com

The microbrewing scene has changed beyond recognition in the eight years since the first edition of this book was published. The sheer number of small independent breweries at work, up and down the land, has now more than doubled to around 1,500.

Ted Bruning, leading beer author, guides you through the practicalities of starting your own microbrewery; from how to brew right through to finding a place of your own.

- How to source the correct equipment
- Advice on developing the necessary skills, raising the finance and finding appropriate premises
- Specialist advice on the design, promotion and marketing of your beer
- Detailed case studies of those who have started their own microbreweries with the pitfalls explained
- Directory of services and suppliers
- **£12.95 plus postage and packing**

# www.posthousepublishing.com

# 03

**Sasma**

Worldwide premium
alcohol supplier.

# We supply the base, **you create the character.**

**Wether you are busy hunting down the perfect texture, or trying to find the ideal equilibrium of botanicals for your blend, Sasma is there to help you get a head start on your product's creation.**

Sasma supplies premium base spirits with 96% alcohol content from first class distilleries all over the world. With our deep market knowledge, we are the partner to help you create your own signature spirit.

Don't let processes such as mashing and fermentation become a bottleneck for your business. Find our far-reaching range of base spirits at **sasmabv.com**.

PREMIUM
ALCOHOL
SUPPLIER

Find your base spirit at **sasmabv.com**

# Green Engineering ®

## RESPECTING  TRADITIONS...

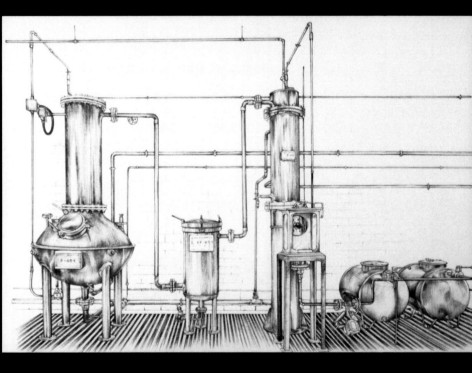

WITH ITS DESIGN DATING BACK TO 1831 POWERED WITH STATE OF THE ART TECHNOLOGIES, OUR UNIQUE MINI CARTERHEAD STILL IS THE HEART OF A BOUTIQUE DISTILLERY PRODUCING THE FIRST VAPOUR INFUSED LONDON DRY GIN MADE IN FLORENCE.

# DELIVERING EXCELLENCE.

DISCOVER THE WIDE RANGE OF SOLUTIONS OFFERED BY A LEADING COMPANY THAT DELIVERS DISTILLATION EQUIPMENT OF ANY SIZE AND FOR ANY SPIRIT, COMBINING STYLISH DESIGN, PATENTED TECHNOLOGIES AND TIMELESS HAND-CRAFTING SKILLS.

# Getting Started

It's going to be a very long journey from your two initial decisions – that distilling is the way forward for you and that gin or whisky or marc or a liqueur is the right product – to the glorious day when the first spirit runs from your very own still. And without putting your house on the market and giving up the day job there are a great many practical – indeed, invaluable – steps between you and your personal Rubicon.

For there's still a great deal of investigatory work you need to do before making the final commitment of actually laying out any capital... and happily for you, your first research projects will be extremely pleasurable. Especially your very first, which involves drinking. Quite a lot of drinking, in fact.

## The learning curve

But this is critical drinking, conducted as much with the brain as with the nose and mouth, to be undertaken soberly and with a number of fixed aims in view. For a start, you need to develop expertise. What are the range of flavours you might expect to experience in gins, or whiskies, or eau-de-vie or liqueurs? What ingredients and processes create these flavours, do you think? How important is balance, and when may one component be allowed to dominate? You also need to cultivate your sense-memory to enable you to identify all the various aromatic and flavour components, and to acquire a considerable reservoir of them; and this can be achieved only by constant practice. Never miss an opportunity, in short, to have a drink.

A large and accurate sense-memory bank is of vital importance in maintaining a consistent product, especially where any sort of blending is involved; for blenders – whether of Cognac, whisky, farm cider or for that matter tea – rely very much on their senses of smell and taste. The constituent parts can differ enormously depending on 101 variables, especially growing and harvesting conditions; and the same might be said if perhaps to a lesser extent of botanicals.

Finally, though, you want to match price with quality. What are the organoleptic differences – the differences in sight, smell, mouthfeel (or texture), flavour and finish – between, say, a supermarket own-label gin and a craft-distilled super-premium brand costing four times as much, or between an own-label blended Scotch and a well-aged single malt? You need to know this because you want to fix a price at which everybody in the supply chain, including yourself, can make a reasonable profit while fulfilling the customers' expectations – the customers, in this case, being pretty sophisticated. Their noses and palates will tell them whether they're getting their money's worth and if their expectations aren't satisfied they won't come back for more.

## Critical tasting

Critical tasting of spirits and liqueurs isn't quite the same as critical tasting of wine or beer, though. The sheer volume of alcohol in neat spirits can mask some of the subtler aromas and flavours; the quantity of sugar in liqueurs can have the same effect.

It is permissible, although frowned upon by some, to water neat spirits down a little (and compulsory if they're export or cask-strength spirits), provided you always use the same amount of water (because in critical tasting, consistency is key). The important thing, though, is never to taste more than four or five at a time and to cleanse your palate thoroughly with plenty of cold water between samples. The Spanish copita is the ideal tasting vessel: its proportions – tall, with a biggish bowl and narrowish brim – allow the volatiles both to start evaporating when the glass is swirled in the hand and then to collect in the neck for nosing. The glassware to be used in serious tastings, by the way, should never simply be reached down from the kitchen shelf: it must always be washed immediately before use in water as hot as you can bear, greasy residues being the particular enemy here, and then thoroughly rinsed of all traces of detergent.

## Visiting distilleries

Almost as pleasurable as comparative or critical tasting is your next piece of homework: visiting as many distilleries as you possibly can. This is more than just a fact-finding exercise during which you get to watch the hardware at work; it's also something of a psychological test that will help you work out how you feel about it. You are, after all, contemplating a life-changing decision – not to mention quite a hefty investment. If visiting working distilleries leaves you completely cold, perhaps you're better off remaining merely an enthusiastic and educated consumer.

Until quite recently you'd have been hard-pressed to find many distilleries to visit unless you were blessed enough to live in Scotland, where around half of the 100+ operating malt whisky distilleries have for many years welcomed tourists with attractions ranging from straightforward guided tours right up to multimedia "experiences". But even then you would in most cases have been treated as a tourist and subjected to a prepared spiel with a fairly high flannel content. All you would have got from it would have been a sketchy outline of the functionings of the various bits of equipment that you could have got a lot more easily, and possibly in considerably more detail, from Wikipedia. (Actually, this isn't entirely fair. For some years now a number of Scottish malt distilleries have run more in-depth tours and critical tasting sessions for more discerning consumers who also, entirely coincidentally, tend to be the consumers with the deepest pockets!)

But assuming you're not based in Scotland, it is now much easier to visit distilleries in England, where 50 are (at time of writing – several more by the time of reading!) registered with HMRC, in Wales, where there are seven (although at time of writing only two are actually operating), and in Northern Ireland, where there are four. Some of these are mainstream distilleries such as James Burrough in Kennington, South London, home of Beefeater, which now has its own visitor centre, and the Bombay Sapphire distillery at Laverstoke, Hampshire and where the visitor centre is planned to be an integral part of the operation. Then of course there's the Blackfriars Distillery in Plymouth, home of Plymouth Gin, which has long been a popular attraction in the city and where the Master Distiller's Tour even allows you to create your own recipe.

Many of the newer distilleries, too, have put tourism at the heart of their marketing: Penderyn is one of the leading tourist attractions in Mid-Wales; while Cornish Cyder near Perranporth, home to the Hicks & Healey Distillery, St George's English whisky distillery near Thetford in Norfolk and the Chase distillery just outside Hereford also offer various levels of guided tour. In most cases, though, the new wave of craft distillers are simply too small to include visitor facilities and their owner-operators are simply too busy to pass the time of day with tourists. What many of them do offer, however, is perhaps far more valuable to their would-be business rivals: small, pre-booked, after-hours tour parties who get to spend quality face-to-face time with the proprietor in person. Get on as many of these as you can, and don't feel too guilty about stealing trade secrets: once you're up and running, the next generation of craft distillers will be doing exactly the same thing to you!

## Experimenting with flavours

There is one further step preparatory to splashing out big-time that any putative distiller must take as a matter of course, and that's product development. Many microbrewers graduated from home brewing, and many others tested their recipes on home-brew rigs before going into production, and still do. Cidermaking and winemaking of all sorts are also perfectly practical at hobby level. But unless you want to incur the displeasure of HMRC, home distilling isn't so straightforward. It is actually possible to get a licence for a miniature test-rig for product development purposes, and equipment of varying degrees of sophistication is available. A retort is a piece of common-or-garden laboratory glassware ideal for experimental purposes; the perfumier's still intended for extracting essential oils from aromatic plants is only a pot-still writ small; and perfectly practical pot-stills of as little as four or five litres' capacity are widely sold by home-brew shops and websites, albeit 'for ornamental use only'. HMRC's discretion over this aspect of issuing licences to distill will be explored in another chapter, but it is possible to request a limited period of approval for the pilot licence to evaluate the product before scaling up.

Alternatively, it is perfectly legal, although far from cheap, to order small quantities of duty-paid neutral alcohol. This won't help you much if you intend to produce either whisky or grape or fruit brandies, but if your chosen product involves infusion or maceration of any kind it will save you a lot of time in the long run. You will of course need a rectifier's and compounder's licence (which HMRC has no powers to refuse). You will also need to "make entry" i.e. a make a list of the rooms and kit you will use and whiz it off to HMRC. That's it. The mere making of the entry (form EX 103 or EX103A) suffices – if you send the entry form registered delivery with evidence of signature from HMRC, the job's done! HMRC does not need to approve anything and once the licence comes through, you're in business. However there is no de minimis limit for the still for requiring a rectifier's licence. Some distillers have been putting it around that anything less than 5 litres is not subject to a licence, which is not true and could land you in trouble.

Even before you have your miniature still and your recti-fier's licence you can start work on your unique and secret blend of botanicals – the juniper-dominated grist of spices, citrus peel and other flavourings that is unique to every gin. With an array of Kilner jars, a quantity of neutral spirit and endless patience you can infuse various botanicals both singly and in blends until eventually you arrive at some-thing very close to the right mixture. It's usual to seethe the botanicals, especially the juniper, in a little warm spirit before setting them to steep. This opens them up and allows the oils to infuse more thoroughly. Then, once you're armed with your miniature still and the correct paperwork, it will be much quicker to arrive at the final version of your recipe.

If, on the other hand, you plan to make macerated liqueurs or flavoured eau-de-vie, the availability of neutral alcohol means that you can effectively create your product at home and get it absolutely right before you take any further steps at all. In Italian supermarkets they sell small bottles of neutral alcohol that families commonly use to concoct their own liqueurs (and which British tourists have been known to mistake for vodka, with hilarious consequences). Steep fruit pulp in neutral alcohol for a few days and let it down to potable strength with water and you have a fruit eau-de-vie. Let the same fruit-infused neutral alcohol down with a blend of syrup and wine or water and you have a liqueur. Within these very loose parameters the permutations are almost endless; the important point here is that you can develop and perfect what is to be your final product before committing yourself to investing your life savings or taking out a large bank loan.

Having said that, you can obtain neutral, odour-free alcohols from Haymankimia (**www.haymankimia.co.uk**). These are derived from the fermentation of either sugar beet molasses, grain or Soil Association certified organic grain. Haymankimia supply 25 litre cans, 205 litre drums or 1000 litre IBCs; prices are available upon request. However, don't forget to factor duty and VAT into your overall cost. Alcohols Ltd, the parent company of the Langley Distillery in Birmingham, will sell you an even smaller quantity – five litres, in fact – for experimental purposes (**www. alcohols.co.uk**) and will give you a price on application. A much cheaper alternative, though, is to use vodka, which will certainly be adequate for experimenting with different grists of botanicals but will not be so accurate when creating liqueur recipes. And the cheaper (and therefore less characterful) the vodka the better.

## Reading all about it

Now you've got this far it's time to relax and put your feet up with a good book – not just for pleasure, but as the first step in your transition from enthusiastic consumer to actual distiller.

There are a number of practical manuals on the market, almost all of them from more enlightened jurisdictions such as New Zealand and some American states where home distilling is perfectly legal. They range from the near-folksy such as Neal and Glenis Boulanger's *Garage Guide to Distilling* to the near-academic such as Stanley and Adam Marianski's *Home Production of Vodkas, Infusions and Liqueurs* and Josef Pischl's *Distilling Fruit Brandy*; but they're all highly informative and reading a good selection of them will give you a head start should you decide to undergo formal training.

Then there's the internet, which is absolutely buzzing with extremely informative sites such as **www.home distiller.org** – again, mostly American – that amount to complete manuals on almost every aspect of distilling and include recipes as well as more technical data than most of us can absorb.

Finally, you should also subscribe to *Harpers*, the wine and spirit trade's monthly magazine (**www.harpers.co.uk**), which has a free online daily update if you're a little on the careful side. Not because it's full of technical information – it isn't – but because taking time to immerse yourself in the world of wines and spirits is all part of the psychological process of transforming yourself from whatever you do for a living right now into the full-time professional distiller you aim to become.

## Formal training

Not all (or even all that many!) craft distillers have been through formal training of any sort. Unless you actually plan to ferment your own wash or wine, both of which are pretty skilled operations, you will find that the theory is very simple and the practice depends as much on experience and judgement as on academic qualifications – although learning when to make the cuts by trial and error only after you've been through the rigmarole and expense of getting the necessary permissions and investing in the necessary plant might perhaps seem a little adventurous.

There is, however, a practical advantage to be had from a broader knowledge of theory than can be derived from a self-taught hands-on "apprenticeship". A little way down the line, when your distillery is thriving, you are almost bound to want to diversify your range. Your original brand might have become stale and have started losing market share to younger, fresher competitors; you might want to start tackling different markets that demand different brands or even different drinks altogether; or you might simply be bored with making and marketing the same product every day. It's at this stage that a sound theoretical understanding both of process and ingredients will demonstrate its value, for product development is a much less hit-and-miss affair – and therefore both faster and cheaper – if you have the expertise to predict (more or less) the likely results of every variation you want to try.

## Heriot–Watt

The acme, of course, is a BSc from the International Centre for Brewing and Distilling at Heriot-Watt University in Edinburgh (**www.icbd.hw.ac.uk**) – preferably followed by an MSc from the same institution. Setting your sights on the BSc course might be a bit ambitious, though: it's full time and can take four years and you will be competing for one of only 30 places with candidates from all over the world. The MSc postgraduate diploma is actually more accessible, provided you have a relevant first degree and can stump up £1,080 per taught course and a fee of £125 per examination: it's part-time and distance-taught (although it can take up to four years).

## Institute of Brewing & Distilling

Probably more suited to your needs – and a good deal cheaper – is a qualification from the Institute of Brewing and Distilling (**www.ibd.org.uk**). There are three levels of qualification: Fundamentals of Distilling, (four days, £875); General Certificate in Distilling (four days, £900); and the Diploma in Distilling (distance-taught followed by three three-hour exams, £995). The IBD runs schools and exam centres all over the country, so you need never stray too far from home. Please note that fees may be subject to VAT.

The Fundamentals qualification describes itself as suitable for non-technical personnel (eg sales, HR) who would benefit from a background knowledge of production or for newcomers who have just started a technical career; but a quick look at the topics covered in this the most basic of the IBD's offering will demonstrate that the description is too modest:

1. Overview – general features of the range of product types including whisk(e)y, brandy, rum, gin and vodka.
2. Raw materials of the principal potable spirits.

3. Fermentation theory.
4. Fermentation technology.
5. Fundamentals of distillation.
6. Distillation technology – batch and continuous.
7. Specific production details for different distilled spirits, including malt and grain whisk(e)y, brandy, rum, gin and vodka.
8. Maturation and blending.
9. Packaging.
10. Distillery co-products.
11. Quality management systems.
12. Quality – process control.
13. Quality – flavour.
14. Quality – hygiene and cleaning systems.
15. Plant maintenance philosophy.
16. Health and safety.
17. Distilling and the environment.

The General Certificate has 20 modules; and the syllabus alone for the Diploma runs to 34 pages. Just reading it is quite an education in itself, actually: it's almost like a road-map setting out the joys and hazards of the journey that lies ahead, and if the sheer complexity of it doesn't put you off, it will fill you with excited anticipation. (The IBD also publishes a magazine, *Brewing & Distilling International*, to which every craft distiller should subscribe.)

## WSET

More consumer-facing are the five levels of qualifications taught and examined by the Wine & Spirit Education Trust (**www.wset.co.uk**). The WSET is really a hospitality industry body, but if your business trajectory leads you towards the restaurant trade you might do well to consider the relevance of its training, especially to front-of-house staff.

## In-house short courses

If you're in such a hurry to get stuck in that none of the above courses suits you, three Scotch whisky distilleries offer short courses that are as much pleasure as business but will provide you with a certain amount of hands-on experience as well as the bare outlines of theory. Three of the newcomers, Kilchoman (**www.kilchomandistillery.com**) on the sacred isle of Islay, Strathearn at Methven in Perthshire and Loch Ewe (**www.lochewedistillery.co.uk**) in the wilds of Wester Ross have five-day schools. Loch Ewe at time of writing will be under new ownership in July 2017 and whether the new owners will provide lessons in distilling is as yet unknown. The course here was always of particular appeal to those prospective distillers of an inquisitive turn of mind, since the whole set-up is consciously designed to evoke and to some extent recreate the pre-1823 era when whisky distilling was an illegal hole-and-corner affair carried out almost on the run. (Don't be put off by its remoteness: it is in the grounds of, and under the same proprietorship as, the Drumchork Lodge Hotel, and accommodation is part of the package.) Springbank Distillery (**www.springbank whisky.com**) also run week long courses and cost £1,200.

That all these short courses should be held in Scotland is no surprise, since they grew out of the tourist side of the whisky industry. That doesn't mean they are of no value to the would-be gin or vodka distiller, however, since the principles and even some of the practices are more or less the same. And for Irish whiskey enthusiasts there is also now a two-day residential course held at Pernod-Ricard's Midleton Distillery – home of Jamesons, Powers, Paddys, Redbreast and other brands.

# Market research

Time spent on reconnaissance is never time wasted, as the military adage has it; and although we will be looking at sales and marketing strategies and techniques in more detail in a later chapter, it's essential to get a reasonable idea of the size and, in particular, the distribution of your prospective markets before you start planning any life-changing investments.

## Demographics

Marketing strategists invariable divide consumers up into groups that you or I would call stereotypes but which they call 'demographics' in order to make the whole thing sound more scientific than it actually is. We civilians tend to find that the way these 'demographics' are characterised is at best absolutely hilarious and at worst horribly patronising, but the truth is that this is the only way to make sense of such enormous and diverse cohorts of consumers, and marketeers don't do it solely to amuse themselves.

It's important to recognise that marketing, however technical its jargon might sound, is an art not a science, and the spirits market is moving and changing so fast that its stereotypes are being knocked over all the time. The tweed-appeal of fine whiskies, gins and brandies is no longer as predominant as it once was.

So question one is: who do you think might most enjoy the product you intend to make? Might they be old bluebloods and retired colonels muttering angrily into their *Daily Telegraphs* (whom we shall now, for brevity's sake, characterise as "colonels" whether they've ever been in the army or not)? Or are they aspirant executives, all gadgets and Beamers and hair-gel ("execs")? Might they be meejah types for whom the adjective hip is not nearly hip enough ("hipsters")? Or earnest Boden catalogue-clad organicists whose weekly trips to Waitrose are but a substitute for the farmers' markets and vegetable box schemes they claim to champion ('Bodens')? Or might they be just plain ordinary people with fully-functioning papillae who know quality when they taste it and are prepared to spend that little bit more to get it (people with taste or 'PWTs')? All very different types, but the one thing they have in common is that they've all got money to spend.

And question two is: where do all these sub-species buy their booze?

This spectrum of demographic stereotypes, remember, doesn't consist of sharply-defined polar opposites but of blurry-edged zones on a continuum; their tastes shade into each other to a surprising extent, both in what they drink and where they drink it. Reading from right to left in cultural terms, as it were, the colonels merge into the Bodens who merge into the PWTs who merge into the execs who merge into the hipsters. You'll find both the colonels and the execs at the golf club, although probably not the Bodens or the PGTs and certainly not the hipsters; you'll find the execs and the hipsters at chic cosmopolitan cocktail lounges, but none of the other groups except perhaps the odd bewildered Boden; and you'll find all of them except the colonels at fusion restaurants and gastropubs where the plates are square and the gravy is called jus. You'll notice that the colonels and the hipsters never meet, except when the hipsters are visiting mum and dad and are obliged to endure Sunday lunch at a real ale pub; but there is one very significant patch of common ground that these two opposites do share, and one that has helped shape the entire craft distilling movement: they both love their gin. Mixed with very different things, granted, but they do love their gin.

## Local retail: on-trade

This brief look at market research will completely ignore

your own online sales and marketing which will, naturally, be of critical importance. What you can do, though, armed with the information given below, is work out the rough number of potential sales outlets both on and off-trade within comfortable delivery distance of your HQ. Local retailers like these may or may not eventually make up a significant proportion of your sales: you are more likely to find a large-ish niche in the region's restaurant trade if you're based in the Cotswolds, say, than if you're based in Cradley Heath. But wherever you happen to operate, local sales have a significance beyond their immediate cash value: they are terrific word-of-mouth generators. Consumers are genuinely proud of local enterprises such as yours, which is a USP independent retailers can and, if they're even slightly canny, do build on. It's also something you can factor into promotions such as distillery visits and – especially popular, for obvious reasons – tutored tasting evenings.

The point of this brief section is to enable you to have a good look at the independent, high-end liquor retail trade within your chosen delivery radius so that you can at least tot up the number of potential stockists. Let's start with the on-trade, and with four categories of retailer: gastropubs, restaurants, cocktail bars and golf clubs.

## Useful guidebooks and websites

The obvious place to find local gastropubs is *The Good Pub Guide*, which is the foodier alternative to CAMRA's *Good Beer Guide* (£12.99) All pubs in GPG are recommended and reviewed by readers and then checked by the publisher's own inspectors. So splash out £15.99 and buy the book.

Unfortunately, there isn't a restaurant guide as definitive in its field as GPG. The best is *Harden's best UK Restaurants* (£15.99). From a market research point of view *Harden's* is better than GFG simply by virtue of being bigger (3,000+ entries compared to GFG's 1,300). One caveat, though, is that *Harden's* includes quite a few chain-owned restaurants whose managers have no discretion to purchase.

You might also, if you're feeling flush, invest in *The Good Hotel Guide* (£20.00) or Johansens to seek out the best luxury and country house hotels in your delivery area; but they might be a bit of an extravagance since these kind of establishments are generally so well-known and so thinly-distributed that **www.yell.com** will give you all the information you need for nothing.

The same is probably true of golf clubs: you probably know all the courses within a 30-mile radius; or if you don't, you know someone who does. Failing that, **www.golftoday.co.uk** and is pretty comprehensive and gives full contact details. And don't neglect golf clubs: the nation's 3,000-odd 19th holes are where all the local well-to-do hang out; they're nearly all independently-owned, so have full stocking discretion and they're very locally rooted and are quite likely to become enthusiastic backers of high-prestige ventures such as yours – especially if you collaborate on exclusive promotions that will add value to their brand.

Which leaves us with cocktail bars. In a sense, this is where it's all happening – this is where the mad mixologists blithely juggle with bottles of £50 gin and the hipsters (and wannabes) queue up to try the latest flavour sensation. Which provides a clue as to the difficulty of identifying bars of this kind – they tend to be ephemeral. There are no printed guides, and national (or for that matter international) websites seem to find it hard to keep up with the changes. Your best bet is to search locally – Googling "cocktail bars leeds", for instance, throws up **www.leeds-list.com**, which appears to be well-informed and up-to-date. Other cities have similarly well-informed sites (and London, of course, has **www.timeout.com.**) The pace of change in venues of this kind has another somewhat depressing effect, and one well-known to microbrewers on the guest ale scene:

you put your heart and soul into securing a new account and two weeks later your place on the bar-back has been taken by the latest new kid in town. Still, throughputs in cocktail bars are very strong, the visibility is very high, and if you're that sort of brand the effort is certainly worth it.

## Local retail: off-trade

To the off-trade now, and a website that is almost comprehensive and is, after the whistles and bells of the Michelin site, refreshingly simple to navigate: **www.ukwinesonline. com**. This simply lists more than 700 wine merchants by county, along with informed reviews and contact details. It really couldn't be easier.

Farmers' markets are another important off-trade outlet for craft food and drink producers of all kinds. They can be patchy – they're extremely vulnerable to poor weather, for one thing – and you do depend very much on the energy and competence of the organisers in publicising them and in administrative minutiae such as such as getting a liquor licence. But they have great appeal, they're potentially terrific word-of-mouth generators, and if you can find a regular stockist in the same town then your market stall not only sells product, it generates future sales too. The best way of tracking them down and finding out what's on in your area is to visit **www.farma.org.uk**, the website of the National Farmers' Retail & Markets Association. This site also allows you to locate farm shops, which range from the open-fronted roadside shed with a single basket of sad courgettes displayed on an upturned crate to huge, sophisticated and lavishly-stocked gourmet gardens of Eden.

And, finally, supermarkets. One word. Don't. Only a handful of the top-shelf spirits brands in the big multiple grocery chains come from genuine independents, and there's a reason for that: supermarkets are a nightmare to deal with unless you're properly set up for it. Throughputs of super-premiums aren't all that impressive, and you may be required to fund occasional promotions. There are a handful of exceptions: Preston-based Booth's (**www.booths.co.uk**) is an old-established family firm with stores throughout the north-west. It's enthusiastic about quality and treats smaller suppliers with respect. Alas, it only has 29 stores. Budgens (**www.budgens.co.uk**) has closer to 200 stores, mainly in eastern and southern England; and it is now an almost entirely franchised operation, which means the stores are owner-operated and have considerable latitude over what they can stock. Budgen's is a pretty middle-market operation by and large, but many of the stores are in quite affluent areas where the franchisees might see the value in stocking locally-produced upmarket food and drink. Contact details of individual stores are on the main site: it's always worth a knock on the door.

How, and even if, you should approach all these various retailers will be dealt with in a later chapter. But at least you can now sit down and make a list (and there's nothing more heartening than a list) of all the potential outlets in your immediate area, which should help you to decide whether the whole operation is even feasible.

# The Winegrowers' Handbook

### A practical guide to setting up a vineyard and winery in the UK

## Belinda Kemp & Emma Rice

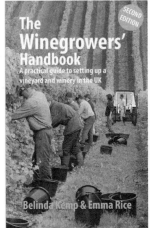

### PUBLISHING SEPTEMBER 2017

- FREE COPY OF THE VINEYARDS MAP OF ENGLAND AND WALES
- The most comprehensive and up-to-date guide on the market
- Written by Belinda Kemp, (Brock University Cool Climate Oenology and Viticulture Institute) and Emma Rice, Director of Wine at Hattingley Valley
- The essential commercial and business manual for potential vineyard owners and winemakers in UK
- Packed with anecdotes and case studies of people who have set up their own vineyards in UK
- Directories of useful websites, government regulations, vineyards, service providers and equipment manufacturers
- Now in its second edition and completely updated and revised
- £10.95 plus postage and packing

# www.posthousepublishing.com

# 04

# A Home of Your Own

In choosing a home for your distillery, there are alternative development paths that need to be decided at the very outset. You might be planning a straightforward working factory, in which case a unit on an industrial estate is ideal. Or you might have grander plans for an on-site shop and/or a visitor centre and restaurant that will attract shoppers and tourists. In the latter case you might already have somewhere appealing in mind: a Victorian model farm building, say, or an old loose-box in the stableyard of a stately home, or even the coach-house of a great Georgian posting inn. The first alternative presents you with rather a dead end: you're never going to attract enough visitors to an industrial estate to justify the additional investment and labour the operation would require. The second alternative leaves you with more flexibility: you can always install your still in an eminently visitable building and then decide that you don't want visitors after all. But whichever alternative you settle on, the first thing you have to do is make sure that you're going to be allowed to use the site as a distillery at all.

## Practicalities

Or rather, the second thing. The first, of course, is whether it will even be possible to site a distillery in the building you've chosen, and that is as much as anything a matter of space. And even though the major items of capital equipment are not, taken individually, all that big, you will still probably need a lot more space than you think.

### Checking for space

The heart of the plant, for most craft distillers, will be a pot still and its condenser, which can be pretty much as big or as small as you need. If you're making gin or other rectified spirits you will also want a rectifying column, which may not have a huge footprint but is likely to be at least four metres tall. If you're a whisky distiller you need two-thirds of a microbrewery (a mashtun and fermenting vessel, but not a brewing copper because you won't be using hops... probably) to produce your wash in. If you're making liqueurs by infusion you want a blending tank that, again, can be as large or as small as you need. And while a four-head manual bottling machine is only about half the size of an upright piano, it's a workstation for two people who need enough room for the empty bottles on one side and the full bottles with labelling machine, bottle-capper and cartons on the other.

If you're buying in neutral spirit or storing large volumes of finished produce before bottling, a 1,000-litre IBC (intermediate bulk container) has a footprint of 1x 1.2 metres and there may one day be several on the premises at a time. Then you need storage for pallets of bottles and consumables such as cardboard cartons, labels and caps; for bulk ingredients such as malt; and for cases of filled bottles. Finally, the office. Quite apart from the usual functions of sales, accounts, HR and so on the paperwork and record-keeping involved in distilling is such that you're going to need a proper office, not just a computer and a filing-cabinet in any old corner: you'll be spending a lot of time there! To sum up, then, while many a pub brewery has been installed in a disused outside loo or cart-shed, you'll need rather more space than that for your distillery, however boutique and bijou.

Whether you settle for the sternly utilitarian or the aesthetically pleasing, you have now to discover whether you're actually going to be allowed to install your stills in it. And that means making friends with two authorities: your district or city or borough council, and Her Majesty's Revenue & Customs.

# Planning permission

Getting planning permission can be a drawn-out, time-consuming, complicated and expensive affair. But it's not half as drawn-out, time-consuming, complicated and expensive as not getting it. Councils vary in their attitude to enforcement: some are absolutely rigorous, while others regard retrospective planning grants more leniently; but the last thing you want is to run the risk of having to undo work you've already done. And if you don't have planning permission, or if you do have it but then breach the terms and conditions set by the council, enforcement is a very real danger. It has even been known to spell the end of a promising business.

If you've gone for the industrial estate option, getting permission to install a distillery in your unit should be relatively straightforward. The site will already have permission for general industrial use – or use class B2 in planning jargon. (B2, in case you're wondering, is general industrial use that might cause detriment to the amenity of the area by reason of "noise, vibration, smell, fumes, smoke, soot, ash, dust or grit". How distillation got classed as B2 when it causes none of these things is anyone's guess, but there you have it). B8, permission for a warehouse, normally goes alongside B2. However there will still be some issues to settle with the local council before you fire up your still.

If B2 use exists – and your solicitor should check this with the vendor or landlord of the site before you exchange contracts – then the exact details of what you propose to do will be classed as "reserved matters" (another useful piece of planning jargon!), which you will need to agree with the council's Development Control department. Other necessary compliances will involve building regulations, health and safety matters and waste water disposal, and you may find that the council won't give you the final go-ahead unless these compliances, especially health and safety and waste water disposal, are fully dealt with in your application.

Getting your planning application under way involves two processes: evaluating the building itself, and evaluating its surroundings. Obviously, it's wise to carry out this exercise as thoroughly as possible before signing a lease or making a purchase – you don't want to be stuck with premises you can't use or face a long, hard and costly battle to get your application through before you can start trading.

## Evaluating the building and its surroundings

As far as the building is concerned, there's quite a long list of boxes to tick. If it's an older property, is it listed? If it is, see 'Listed Building Consent' below. Can it jump through all the relevant health and safety hoops? How good is the vehicle access? Is there room on the site for all employees, visitors and deliveries to park off-street and for vehicles to manoeuvre, e.g. for articulated lorries to reverse?

As for its surroundings, is it in an area where general industrial use is allowed by the Local Development Framework? Is permission for shop (A1) or bar (A3) use likely to be granted, or does the LDF frown on the volume of traffic these uses are likely to generate? Is the premises in a conservation area, an Area of Outstanding Natural Beauty or a National Park? How many traffic movements on and off site do you envisage? Can you control noise and emissions to the satisfaction of local residents, if there are any?

## Preparing your application

Getting planning permission is – supposedly, at least – somewhat more straightforward these days than it used to be, and thanks to the web, it's also much easier to get the information you need. At **www.planningportal.gov.uk** you'll find a pretty exhaustive guide to planning matters: it even enables you to apply online and includes a fee calculator to help you work out roughly how much the council will charge you. It also has links to other sites detailing, for instance, national policy on converting surplus agricultural buildings to other employment-related uses (Public Planning Guidance note or PPG7). Since 2002 there has been a presumption that councils should approve 'well-conceived farm diversification proposals, particularly involving the re-use of existing buildings for business purposes'. Another useful link is to the Royal Town Planning Institute's site, which includes a list of planning and development consultants. Hopefully you won't need one, but if your application is any less than perfectly straightforward, you very well might!

In law, councils have to determine your application within eight weeks of receiving it, but they have the power to extend the permitted period under certain circumstances. If they do, you can appeal to the Secretary of State, but it's rather self-defeating as the appeal will almost certainly take longer than the council would have, left to itself. So if you want your application to be determined as quickly as possible – and if you want to be sure of getting the right result – then everything hinges on thorough preparation and good communication. What this means, in effect, is that the whole planning process will take a lot longer than eight weeks – eight months, more like! – but the vast bulk of the work will be done before your application actually goes in.

The important thing is not to be afraid. Some people think the council is there to frustrate them or tie them up in red tape, and the only way to get an application through is to sneak it under the town hall's radar somehow. And while it's true that councils can be awkward if they want to, and that there are more formalities to go through than at the State Opening of Parliament, in essence the council is there to help you and even has an obligation to make suitable provision for industrial developments such as yours. The grounds on which applications can be refused or substantially varied are finite; and if you discover in advance what they are, you shouldn't find it too hard to put together an application that is more or less bound to succeed.

## Local Development Framework

First, check the relevant sections of the LDF (or, if your council is a little old-fashioned, the Local Plan) thoroughly. This is available from the city, borough, or district council, or on its website. Unfortunately it's not a single document, but a collection of them: however, the site should be fairly easy to navigate. The LDF or Local Plan is divided into two sections: general policy across the whole district, and more specific policies location by location. Armed with this information, you should at least be able to tell quite quickly whether the building you have in mind is likely to be acceptable for B2 use.

However, the Planning Portal site and LDFs are very general documents and paint rather a rosy picture of the planning process. Things can and do go wrong, especially in urban centres where there is strong competition for development sites, or when planning officers decide that the proposed use is unsuited to the building. (Or – quite common these days – there simply aren't enough planning officers to handle the increasing number of applications such as yours!) Another stumbling-block you might face if your long-term plans include the development of a shop, restaurant or visitor centre is the thorny question of mixed use. A lot of local planners have been very slow to get their heads round the concept that a single business premises might want A1 or A3 use for part of the site and B2/B8 for another. Planners do seem to be getting less resistant to the idea than previously, but if mixed use does seem to be presenting a problem, you can usually overcome it by arming yourself with a good number of precedents, preferably fairly local.

## The Planning Officer

There is no way of guaranteeing that these kind of problems won't arise but one way of reducing the risk is to open a good channel of communications with the planning officer working on your application. You will have to pay an administration fee to cover the costs of your application anyway, but some councils will charge extra for an initial consultation with your planning officer. However, as it's this very officer who will recommend acceptance or rejection of your plan to the council's Development Control Committee, the extra charge is probably money well spent.

Involving this officer in the evolution of your distillery makes it almost as much his or her baby as yours; in fact planning officers whose work is mostly pretty humdrum stuff have been known to get enthusiastically engaged by the prospect of handling something a bit out of the ordinary. So by the time the application is ready to be formally considered, the two of you should have made it almost watertight. Of course, this process may itself have its ups and downs; but remember, if your planning officer flatly vetoes an idea of yours, it's not out of bloody-mindedness (probably not, anyway) but out of a deep knowledge of local policies and a very shrewd understanding of what will or won't get through.

The planning officer's main concern, after the suitability of the building itself, will be the impact of your distillery on its neighbours, especially if there are any residents in the immediate area. This concern is partly met by the LDF's approved uses for the locality. But the officer will also be interested in noise, smells and other emissions, waste discharge and any changes you propose to the appearance of the building, particularly if you will need external equipment such as extractors, flues and tankage.

## Local consultation

A large part of the process involves consultation, and not just with the neighbours. Of course, you will have to advertise your application both in the local press (another expense!) and on the application premises, to give them the chance to object if they fear your plans will threaten the 'amenity' of the area. But the grounds on which they can object are limited by statute, and the planning authority is specifically instructed (see the Planning Portals website again) that the mere number of objections is irrelevant. The determination of planning applications depends on what the law actually says, not what the neighbours would rather it said; – the number of objections is immaterial.

The main consultation, however, will not be with the neighbours but with other statutory bodies: the local council's own environmental health department; the county council as highways authority; the police and fire services; the parish council; the Environment Agency; and the Health & Safety Executive. This is the part of the process that really takes the time, and it's these agencies that are likeliest to have objections. If your application conforms to the LDF and is made out thoroughly and in proper form, you should hopefully clear this last hurdle and be able to start distilling.

## Listed Building Consent

If you're planning more than a standalone factory and want to convert somewhere quaint enough to attract visitors, you will almost certainly find that the premises is listed and will need Listed Building Consent from English Heritage before the necessary alterations can be made. And while gaining consent is another long drawn-out procedure, it is by no means impossible to get.

Just as restrictions on the conversion of agricultural buildings to light industrial use have been eased over the past 35 years, so the regulations aimed at pickling historic buildings in aspic have been, to an extent, relaxed. English Heritage,

Historic Scotland and Cadw are particularly keen to see that historic farm buildings unsuited to the demands of modern agriculture should be kept in use, because the alternative is dereliction and, eventually, demolition. Getting permission to turn Georgian or early Victorian cow-byres and wagon-sheds into retail units is no longer much of a problem; light industrial use, especially if it is food-related and/or connected to an activity (such as wine-making) already being carried on at the premises, is therefore not only permissible but even encouraged provided the necessary alterations are sensitively planned. English Heritage has a number of publications and guides relating to the conversion and maintenance of redundant historic farm buildings in the 'professionals' section of its website, **www.english-heritage.org.uk**: *Conversion of Traditional Farm Buildings: a Guide to Good Practice* is particularly enlightening. Its attitude to the conversion to light industrial use of the outbuildings of great country houses, which are in general more thoroughly listed than their home farms – Grade I or Grade II* rather than plain old Grade II – might be described as a little less relaxed. Nevertheless English Heritage prefers these august piles to work for their living rather than crumble away; its approach to conversions that alter the appearance or character of such houses is, it says, less policy-driven and more case-by-case. Its discretion in such cases is broad; but its instinct is, not unnaturally, to be a bit of a stickler.

Strictly speaking, your application for Listed Building Consent is an entirely separate matter from your change of use application as it's covered by different laws; but in practice the two applications can be submitted at the same time. They remain separate applications, though, and the outcome of one doesn't affect the outcome of the other. You can be granted listed building consent on the grounds that your proposals don't affect the building's character, but still be refused change of use permission on the grounds that, say, vehicle access is inadequate. Refusal of either application can be challenged, so if you're knocked back on the one but get through on the other, the game's not necessarily up.

## Shop, restaurant and visitor centre

If your business plan envisages any sort of retail operation on the site, you will need to apply for uses A1 (shop), A3 (restaurant/cafe), A4 (bar) and possibly D1 (museum/exhibition space). In a listed building or complex of listed buildings the same considerations as above will apply, but one aspect of any retail development that the planners will pay particular attention to is the additional traffic it generates as customers and suppliers come and go.

If you are hoping to develop some sort of retail operation or visitor attraction some way further down the line – once the distilling business has established itself, say, or when investment funds become available – it's an essential precaution to check your Local Plan/LDF and to confer with the planning officer handling your application at the very outset to make absolutely certain it will even be possible. Getting a liquor licence is a different matter again and will be dealt with in the chapter on marketing. Suffice it to say that you may not sell any alcohol from the premises, not even to tour parties and not even online (a pratfall that has caught out quite a few microbrewers in the past) without a licence.

## Appeals

If you fail in any of your planning applications the obvious thing is to appeal, and you have six months from the rejection of your application to do so. Once again, the Planning Portal contains all the details you need – you can even appeal online! Appeals are handled by the Planning Inspectorate, which appoints an independent inspector to whom you can both state your own case and comment on

## Case Study – Kilchoman
### www.kilchomandistillery.com

Look at a roadmap of Islay and you'll quickly realise that Kilchoman is not only the island's newest distillery (by 124 years, actually); it's also the hardest to get to. Lagavulin, Laphroaig, Ardbeg – why, they're virtually in downtown Port Ellen. Bruichladdicch, Bowmore – Islay's motorway, the A846, runs past their front doors. Even Bunnahabhain is only a bike-ride from Port Askaig.

But Kilchoman! You have to leave the safety of the A846 at Bridgend. Actually, it's not that remote at all. It's less than 10 miles from Bridgend and there's only one right and two left turns to remember, so anyone with a car and the ability to memorise the simplest of directions should get there in no time at all. And the location was very carefully chosen.

"Grass to glass" is an aspect of localism that has inspired many of the new wave distillers, and when in 2004 independent bottler Anthony Wills decided to set up a distillery of his own he wanted to be able to grow the barley to make the malt to ferment into the wash that would go into the still. He even built his own maltings so the entire operation could be conducted on site. This virtual self-sufficiency, he felt, epitomised the 500-year-old Scottish tradition of distilling on the farm. (Even his distillery manager was locally-grown: John McLellan had worked for 21 years at Bunnahabhain.)

The first thing Anthony needed, therefore, was a farm; and since his wife Kathy was a native of Islay, that was where they started looking. They were fortunate enough to find Rockside, which is not only attractive in its own right but is beautifully located on the glorious white sand beach of Machir Bay and, better yet, already had a reputation as a grower of first-class malting barley. In 2005 they converted it into a distillery, and the first new make was filled into cask on 14 December that year. (Just two days later exactly the same operation was carried out at another very similar "grass to glass" whisky distillery, but on the other side of Scotland on the Cuthbert family farm at Daftmill, near Cupar in Fife).

The fact that Rockside is on Islay was a prime consideration. "Islay may only have had seven distilleries before we came along, but every single one of them is known to whisky lovers the world over and between them they have made Islay into a hugely successful brand in its own right," says Anthony. "In terms of location, coming to Islay was perhaps the most important decision we made. The very name gave us a great head start."

But the magic of the name, and the huge interest it would arouse around the world – imagine any enthusiast not being desperate to get their hands on a new single malt from Islay! – was only one reason for coming to the island. The other was tourism. Right from the beginning Kilchoman was equipped with a shop and cafe, and although tours have to be limited both in frequency and size it has proved a very popular draw.

"Oh, we're not all that hard to find," says Anthony. "The main difficulty is getting to Islay in the first place. Once you're here you find it's only a small island and it's really very easy to drive round.

"For us, tourism has always been terrifically important in the scheme of things. Islay is a big tourist destination: tourism plays a huge part in its economy and the distilleries are an important part of its attraction."

"People come here and then tell their friends about us. It creates an extraordinary amount of awareness," says Anthony. "You could even say it was one of the most important parts of our marketing."

the planning authority's statement of case. The inspectorate also appoints a case officer who will help you by telling you what documentation to present and when, although when dealing with unfamiliar, complex and jargon-ridden rules and regulations you may well feel you need the (expensive) advice of an experienced surveyor or planning consultant.

An appeal is the only way to overcome refusal of listed building consent, but if you are refused change of use permission, a quicker and cheaper option is to find out what the council didn't like about your initial application, amend it accordingly and resubmit. If you do this within 12 months there will be no fee, and as objections to the original application are considered to have been dealt with already they can't be submitted again. This is the way large corporations wear down local objectors – they simply present slightly altered applications again and again until their opponents either run out of new objections or are simply too exhausted to continue. That's perhaps not quite what you have in mind, but if you have been refused on minor or technical grounds this is the simplest solution. Once you have been granted planning permission, you have three years to act on it before it expires.

## Distilling – HMRC's requirements

In Notice 39 regulating the production of spirits, HMRC stresses that you should get its approval of your proposed premises before you sign a conveyance or lease and commit yourself to parting with any money. In fact, legally you must acquire the distiller's licence (which is a simple application using the on-line form L5) and, before producing spirits, apply to have premises, plant and processes approved by HMRC. In practice, the licence and approval applications are treated in parallel (see Notice 39 concerning approvals).

That means, as we shall see, submitting extraordinarily

detailed plans and drawings of the exact layout and describing and listing all the equipment you intend to install and the processes you will undertake. This requirement may seem, on the face of, like just another piece of irritating red tape, but actually having to sit down and plan your plant in minute detail concentrates the mind wonderfully and will prove a marvellous aid to putting together your business plan. HMRC has the discretion to apply conditions to the licence and approval but has reacted well to the joint industries' representations to expect minimal additional conditions to be imposed on any and all approvals (which HMRC has to be able to justify in law – there have to be very good reasons for any additional conditions to be imposed).

Bear in mind that a distillery is somewhat different to a brewery, a winery or a cider mill. The distillery is not itself a place of revenue security as a 'tax warehouse' as defined in UK law (although it has to be licensed and approved). Rather, the vat in which the spirits are collected after production in the distillery is the 'tax warehouse' and has to be subject to the approval of HMRC and, actually, an entry made of that vessel/place as well. The spirits collected and accounted for in the distiller's warehouse have then to be immediately removed to a 'full' excise warehouse (which is usually a maturation warehouse associated with the distillery but may be a temporary warehouse where spirits are held before being sent on for maturation – see below).

HMRC's concerns are dictated not by the antiquity or appearance of the premises, nor by the impact on the neighbourhood of its use as a distillery, but by its security and, of high importance, the ability of the distiller to raise and maintain accurate records and accounts. In what might perhaps be a throwback to the whisky wars of the 18th century when the Excisemen or 'gaugers' were pitted against the Scottish moonshiners, HMRC is almost paranoid that not a single drop of dutiable spirit should leave the distillery without being duly accounted for. Notice 39 sternly reminds you that you are responsible for the security (not only physical security but also financial security, which as we shall see must in most cases by covered by a third-party guarantor not in the distiller's warehouse) of the spirit until the duty is paid, and that you must pay duty on any losses you cannot explain. It goes on to recommend a package of strict security measures and checks with the implied caveat that if you don't follow its 'recommendations' you won't get your licence.

## Premises security

The first recommendation, naturally, is that the premises' perimeter and the building itself are secure against casual or forced entry; that the security measures are such that they will show any signs of forced entry; and that these precautions should be regularly reviewed. But what follows clearly stems from HMRC's belief that the real threat to its revenues comes not from burglars or ram-raiders but from you: proprietors seeking to make a bit of extra profit on the quiet by selling a few litres on the black market (it has happened, you know!) or employees pilfering the odd drop here and there to accompany their evening's TV viewing. Anyway, HMRC requires that access to the stillroom and warehouse should be restricted, that the openings of all vessels and plant should be locked or sealed, preferably with tamper-evident closures, and that access to all areas and vessels should be controlled.

## Inspections

And just to make sure you're not on the fiddle, Notice 39 "expects all plant to be accessible, readily identifiable, and with the exception of working stills, capable of being opened as required for inspection; and that all wash backs, feints receivers and spirit receivers should be gauged and

## Application for a distiller's licence and approval of distillery plant and process with form DLA1

The form is intended to be filled in online at **https:// public-online.hmrc.gov.uk/lc/content/xfaforms/profiles/ forms.html?contentRoot=repository:///Applications/Indi- rectTax/1.0/DLA1&template=DLA1.xdp**

If you need further help or have any other queries, call their Helpline on 0300 200 3700

The form is designed to be filled in on screen. You must answer all the questions except those marked 'optional'. You can't save the form but once you've completed it you'll be able to print a copy and post it.

In order to produce spirits you must apply for a distiller's licence and obtain approval of your distillery plant and process providing the following information.

- Application for a distiller's licence
- Application for approval of Plant and Process
- Location of proposed distillery
- Full description of the manufacturing process, including size of still
- The number and description of the vessels used in the manufacturing process, their capacity and use of all plant
- Your intended source of raw materials and the range of products you intend to produce
- Plan of premises
- Product storage
- Application for warehouse approval
- If you plan to store the product on your premises you will also need to apply for authorisation as a warehouse-keeper and excise warehouse approval. These applications can be found on the HMRC website.

calibrated, with calibration tables readily available." So you are being watched. But don't be too nettled by this overt lack of trust in your probity: all distillers get to know their regional HMRC officers pretty well and mostly say that they're quite nice, actually. (Although however friendly they turn out to be, don't be tempted to give them a bottle of your product for Christmas: there is such a thing as Misconduct in a Public Office!)

But naturally, it's not quite as simple as that. Paragraph 2.4 of Notice 39 requires you to apply for approval of plant and process by supplying the location of the proposed distillery, a full description of the manufacturing process, the number of vessels to be used in the manufacturing process and a description of each item, including dimensions, and a plan of the premises. It concludes: Reading between the lines, HMRC officers have enormous latitude in deciding to grant or withhold your licence, to set the conditions by which you may operate and, after granting the licence, whether to vary the conditions. Getting your application through is therefore – as with so much of the planning process – a matter of long negotiation and (however grudging) full co-operation; and two points are worth bearing in mind here.

To be fair, HMRC has an interest in seeing your venture through to fruition because of the duty and other taxes you will pay, so its officers are (or should be) naturally inclined to be helpful and positive. HMRC has also become more used to dealing with new applications – the problem now is a shortage of resources to deal with the large number of new applicants and applications for variations to existing approvals. The vexed question of minimum permissible still capacity is one we shall deal with in the next chapter, but officers are wont to confuse departmental policy with statute, and their word should not always be taken as final without reference to the actual law. Getting your licence and approval should not now be a long and drawn-out affair, especially for gin rectifiers who buy in their ethanol.

Since the craft distilling movement got under way HMRC has unbent to a remarkable degree and has shaken off the idea that distilleries have to be discrete industrial premises surrounded by barbed wire and patrolled by man-eating Alsatians. Of the craft gin pioneers, Sam Galsworthy and Fairfax Hall founded Sipsmiths in a lock-up in Hammersmith (although they've now moved to bigger premises in Chiswick); Ian Hart founded Sacred Gin in his house in Highgate, where it still is; and Will and Lucy Lowe run the remarkable Cambridge Distillery – the "gin tailor" making bespoke gins for individual customers – from their home in the city, even growing many of their botanicals in their garden.

But while HMRC will look kindly on these very small-scale rectifying operations, it will still take its time over approving the details. Until HMRC became more familiar with its own law (which is highly flexible) and trade needs, things took their due course. In the case of the Lowes, the licensing process took a whole year; in other cases it has taken two. But the congestion has definitely eased as HMRC gets more and more accustomed to handling applications: Alex Wolpert signed the lease on the Bow Wharf Bar in Hackney, east London, in January 2014 and was distilling by August. Since then, many more have been licensed and approved.

## Warehousing

If you are planning to make whisky or brandy or other spirits in your own distillery, you will almost certainly need a duty-suspended premises in which to remove and deposit the initial produce of the distillery following the collection of the spirits in the distiller's warehouse. HMRC permits such premises to be approved as excise warehouses under section 92 of the Customs and Excise Management Act 1979

(CEMA) and – using powers of discretion – permits a restricted approval to be given for the initial storage of the spirits as a trade facility (TF) criterion warehouse. This policy permits the spirits to be temporarily stored (or operated on) but HMRC's policy also requires that the goods must be duty-paid by a stated period (usually within 30 days of production) or sent under duty-suspension to another fully licensed excise warehouse/bond or general storage and distribution (GSD) warehouse. NB Both TF and GSD policy warehouses are "proper" excise warehouses approved under CEMA s92, a point often lost on HMRC.

If you intend to mature spirits in your own warehouse, you will need approval under the GSD policy to mature the spirits, but you will then encounter the need for a premises guarantee, which is a major bugbear for new entrants. Many, if not most, new distillers send their spirits to mature off-site to avoid having to find the premises guarantee (but which incurs transport and then storage costs at the third-party warehouse). We will look at that below.

You will undoubtedly have in the back of your mind a delicious vision of cobwebby oak barrels slumbering away in glorious duty suspension in a dimly-lit old warehouse, slowly surrendering the angel's share while the aldehydes and other noxious compounds gradually break down and the colours and flavours of the ancient wood leach, molecule by molecule, into your new make and transform it over the years into a... yes, well, that's quite enough of that. It's a lovely dream, but one practical detail you will need to bear in mind while house-hunting is that tiers of beautiful oak casks take up a lot of space. You'll need a facility with enough room for at least three years' output and plenty of space to work round your barrels as well, because a full oak cask of a minimum of 700 litres capacity weighs very nearly a ton and requires a forklift to shift.

You will also, without doubt, have fairly strong

opinions about the ideal climatic conditions in which your stock ought to mature. This is a thorny subject, because there's not a lot of science to back it up, but some distillers swear by a warehouse that's moist, cool and faces north, while others swear by the exact opposite with equal conviction. Some maintain that a maritime location is absolutely essential to get that briny tang; others call that utter nonsense. Maturation, you see, is the aspect of whisky distilling where romance really comes into its own – which is no bad thing, since romance is a very large part of the sales pitch. (There's also a financial consideration, since HMRC requires a guarantor, normally your bank, to put up a not inconsiderable bond on maturing stocks.)

Gin and vodka rectifiers who produce under duty suspension may do so in a trade facility excise warehouse (rectification/compounding being standard operations in warehouse under the warehousing regulations) and require considerably less warehousing space than makers of whisky or brandy since their stock doesn't need to mature. so HMRC recognises the fact by categorising them as "trade facility warehouses" where newly-bottled stock can be held for a short while – exactly how long is a matter for individual negotiation, although 30 days seems to be a generally-accepted norm – before the duty has to be paid. The "warehouse," even in a fairly productive white spirits distillery, need not be much more than a loading bay, but when choosing a premises do have an eye to the requirements of future expansion – or, for those of a pessimistic bent, to the backlog of stock that might build up should an order fall through or a customer change suppliers or even fail to pay up.

## Excise warehouse authorisations and approvals

The real control of spirits (and how duty is accounted for and charged on them) takes place within the excise warehousing system, i.e. after production in the distillery. This is its own world, mainly based on consolidated ancient laws comprising CEMA s92, the (creaking) Excise Warehousing (Etc.) regulation 1988 (EWER) and more recent law, including the Warehousekeepers and Owners of Goods in Warehouse Regulations 1999 (WOWGR) and the Excise Goods (Holding, Movement and Duty Point Regulations 2010 (HMDP) – There is a high degree of risk for getting a single thing wrong under these provisions – liability to the duty for "ticking the wrong box" and savage civil penalties even for inadvertent errors as "wrong-doing" under the Finance Act 2008 Schedule 41. So don't be tempted to skimp on your legal duties either before or after being approved by HMRC.

Whatever your warehousing requirements, you need to read Notice 196: Authorisation of Warehousekeepers and Approval of Premises very, very carefully. It's a monster document: even the précis that makes up Appendix II of this book will keep you entertained for hours, but it's also invaluable at this stage because it will give you an extremely detailed preview of the obstacle course awaiting you. You will also need to read Notice 197, which deals with the actual "holding and movement" of excise goods and accounting for the duty etc. Moreover, there is much interweaving between the two notices (which until a few years ago used to be a single notice – and it shows!). The key points are summarised below.

Before even applying, HMRC requires you to be a "fit and proper" person – that is you (or your associates / directors) don't have any unspent convictions, have paid all your taxes and are a good egg generally. The full requirements are set out for the first time in Notice 196 (January 2016), paragraph 3.2 (especially the third section within that very large and widely-ranging paragraph). HMRC is looking to exclude fraudsters from the system, who may use the distillery regime as the soft underbelly to infiltrate and divert duty-suspended alcohol.

Assuming you are fit and proper, you must then (a) apply to be authorised by HMRC as an excise warehousekeeper under WOWGR (form EX61) and (b) apply for approval of your premises as an excise warehouse (there can be multiple premises on the application) – form EX69. The application forms are currently somewhat deficient for what HMRC really needs to know, so it is best to send an explanatory accompanying letter about your business. Crucial to this is your business plan. HMRC will expect you to have done proper research into the market for your product and usually requires letters of intent or expressions of interest. They are, understandably, not impressed with vague plans, so the more thorough, the better.

Perhaps the most important thing of all is the raising and maintenance of appropriate accounts and records. HMRC does most of its control through excise traders' records, so your warehouse stock accounts and records must be in accordance with Notice 196 paragraph 3.3.2, as required by the Excise Warehousing (Etc.) Regulations 1988. If your records are not satisfactory, you will never be approved. The problem for new applicants is that HMRC does not tell you what the records should look like (HMCE did away with their own entry books for traders over 25 years ago). It will nevertheless assist you; in addition, consultants can provide pro forma record-keeping templates. You will also need to comply with the 'core' revenue trader's accounts and records regulations, including keeping a duty account. This is explained in HMRC's Notice 206 – it is imperative to comply with this notice.

As an excise warehousekeeper, you will have to be registered for the electronic Excise Movement and Control System (EMCS), which you must do when you receive your approvals from HMRC. The EMCS holds all your details and is used for the duty-suspended movement of excise goods nationally and intra-EU. There is no other option for the administration and control of such movements. EMCS was set up as a computerised real-time anti-fraud measure, but has proved a very helpful system for legitimate businesses to move goods around. HMRC has a portal for EMCS on line that is free to use. The EMCS help-desk is also very obliging, which for new users is a blessing.

In terms of physical security, you will be expected to operate to a high level of probity within a secure environment. That said, an excise warehouse isn't Fort Knox and HMRC can't be unreasonable about what is truly and proportionately "secure". After all, for your own fire and theft insurance you must have decent security and precautions and in any case, Customs can assess for duty on any losses you can't account for (and if you keep "losing" stock, HMRC can withdraw your approval, and serve you right!).

## Storing goods in third-party warehouse

One hugely important thing to be aware of is the need to be approved and registered by HMRC separately if you intend to deposit and store your own goods in another (third party) excise warehouse. This possibility arises if you operate a trade facility warehouse and don't want to pay the duty on your produce within 30 days (or whatever period is stipulated by HMRC) – in which case you need to move your product off-site under duty suspension. You can't just dispatch the goods you own to another warehouse – you must first apply to be approved and registered with HMRC as an owner of goods in warehouse and receive a certificate of such registration (often called a WOWGR certificate). Because of the huge risk and heavy sanctions for non-compliance, no reputable third-party warehouse will deal with you unless you hold a WOWGR certificate, so don't forget to apply if you even think you may need such approval. WOWGR is also covered in Notice 195 section 5. You make application on form EX60.

## Due Diligence

Given the high level of alcohol fraud, HMRC has recently imposed a condition on all alcohol businesses to carry out a formal Due Diligence policy on persons involved anywhere in the supply chain – see Notice 196 section 10. It is placing a high degree of emphasis on this condition, so although it may seem like overkill, it's no longer enough to carry out standard credit checks on customers: you are expected to assess the likelihood of there being any illegality underlying any business you do, and ensure you put in place a Due Diligence policy, carry it out and review it. In many ways, it is like a loosely-worded version of the anti-money laundering regulations.

## Premises guarantee

Before giving final approval to operate an excise warehouse, HMRC requires a guarantee to be in place as a precondition. This is known as the premises guarantee and has replaced the old requirement for a bond. There is no longer any such thing as a "bonded warehouse" in UK excise law – it is an excise warehouse where goods are held in duty suspension. Somewhat confusingly, all places where excise goods are produced, deposited, operated on and moved are defined as tax warehouses in EU law, which has been transposed into UK law. Thus breweries, wineries, cider-mills, excise warehouses and distillers' warehouses are all defined as tax warehouses. But HMRC only applies a mandatory requirement for a guarantee to excise warehouses where spirits have to be held and duty accounted for and paid under warehousing law.

The premises guarantee is not mandatory under EU law and is subject to HMRC's discretionary powers under CEMA s157. The guarantee is seldom required in full by HMRC; rather, it covers a small percentage of the potential duty of the goods held in duty suspension. Nevertheless, you will always be liable for all the duty on unexplained losses from the warehouse not due to natural cause (so you need to be well insured). The guarantee is a fallback that HMRC can all on from your guarantor (always a bank or insurance company. If there is still a debt, HMRC as an unsecured creditor will enforce it promptly, a position best avoided in the first place. HMRC's policy and requirements for premises guarantees are set out in paragraph 4.5 of Notice 196. It is not clear or certain (if you carefully read the details) exactly what the level of guarantee should be for TF warehouses, since HMRC says (almost as an afterthought) it will base the guarantee on throughput, but does not say what period of throughput or what level of guarantee. In practice, if you keep your stockholding per month below £100,000 HMRC will not require a guarantee, and paying your duty within 30 days or moving surplus stock under duty suspension to another GSD warehouse should enable you to keep it under that £100,000.

If, however, you are looking to mature spirits on your own site (this is especially relevant to whisky producers), your stockholding will very quickly exceed £100,000 stockholding and will need to consider approval under GSD criteria. This requires a minimum guarantee of £250,000 (forget the "nil" and £100k levels set out in Notice 196 – they don't apply to new applicants). Bear in mind that your guarantor will have the £250k as full exposure on its books and will therefore demand to be indemnified against that risk. In other words, you will have to find that £250k to fund the guarantor (who will also charge a premium for the service of providing a guarantee – if they indeed offer to provide it. This often comes as a rude shock to applicants who have not factored that level of investment into their business plan. Some have even foundered altogether on this hidden rock.

If you can fund a guarantee, you will be eligible for a 50 per cent reduction of its level after two years "no-claims" and a reduction to nil after a further two years. In fact, most established excise warehousekeepers operate under "nil premises security."

## Movement guarantee

The movement guarantee is a mandatory condition when excise goods are moved between approved premises under duty suspension (i.e. under EMCS). This guarantee can be provided by the warehousekeeper of dispatch (you, if approved), or the transporter or the owner of the goods. If you're dispatching your own goods from your own warehouse, it is best to find a haulier who has such a guarantee. If you have to provide the guarantee, HMRC's conditions are set out in Notice 197 paragraph 10.2. The minimum level of security required for movement guarantees is £20,000.

05

# Nuts and Bolts

The daunting array of new and unfamiliar super-premium gins with their equally new and unfamiliar grists of botanicals on the top shelf of Tesco's spirits aisle might well lead you to think that craft distillers had taken over the world. But things aren't quite as they seem. Many of the new super-premiums come from long-established big distillers such as William Grant & Sons (best-known for Glenfiddich single malt whisky but also the begetter of Hendrick's Gin) and G&J Drinks (perhaps more familiar under its old name, G&J Greenalls) of Warrington. Many more (as we saw in Chapter One) are contract-distilled by specialists such as Thames Distillers of Clapham, Langley Distillery in Birmingham and G&J's own contract division, Essential Drinks, on behalf of brand proprietors who seldom have occasion to stray into the distillery itself.

## Contract distillers

In fact very few of the bigger nationally and internationally distributed new-wave gin brands come from small independent distillers, and this has raised something of a question. If you are the owner of a successful international brand that is actually made for you by a contract distiller, can that brand legitimately be described as a "craft" product?

Well, it all depends on your definition of "craft". If it implies a hands-on artisanal owner-operator who borders on the obsessive-compulsive, then no it can't. If it implies that the distiller who actually makes the stuff is an artist in his (or in the case of G&J, her) own right, then yes it can. Langley (**www.alcohols.co.uk**) has been a distillery since 1920, before which the premises was a brewery; its oldest still celebrated its centenary some years ago. The proprietor of Thames Distillers (**www.thamesdistillers.co.uk**), Charles Maxwell, is virtually gin royalty: his family owned the Finsbury Distillery in the City of London for untold generations until 1992 when Matthew Clark bought and closed it; and gin being in his blood, he founded Thames in 1995 with two small stills, Tom Thumb and Thumbelina, rescued from another old City distillery. Joanna Moore, master distiller at G&J (**www.essential-drinks.com**) since 2006, may be a comparative newcomer but has a proven track-record of formulating and producing not only giant own-label brands for supermarket chains but highly-praised small-batch premium gins as well.

## Smaller contractors

These grand credentials, though, are irrelevant if you think that the business of small independent distillers is to distill, not to get contractors to distill for them. For the majority of craft distillers that is indeed true – but not for all. Julian Temperley of Burrow Hill Cider, whose Somerset Royal Cider Brandy kicked the whole movement off, has distilled for a number of other cidermakers including, most famously, the monks of Ampleforth Abbey. He also, during a run of good vintages in the early 1990s, made brandy for a number of vineyards such as Moor Lynch of Dorset that found they had a surplus of wine on their hands.

Julian Temperley's example is now being followed by others such as the English Spirit Company of Dullingham in Cambridgeshire, (**www.englishspiritdistillery.com**) and Mike Hardingham of the Ludlow Vineyard & Distillery at Clee St Margaret in Shropshire (**www.ludlowdistillery. co.uk**). Since installing his own German-made 200-litre pot still and four-plate rectifying column Mike has not only made his own grape, apple, and pear brandies and eau-de-vie but also contract-distills for a number of other winemakers in the region. The extra income from contract distilling, he says, helps him justify the investment he originally made in buying and installing his still.

However, it's well worth remembering that the larger and better-known contractors can also oblige with quite short runs: 6,000 bottles in the case of Thames and 2,500 in the case of Langley. And 2,500 bottles is only a lot if it doesn't sell! The activities of these contract distillers are not confined to rectifying gin, either: Langley could even make whisky, if anyone asked it to. (Not that anyone has... yet!)

But if the role of contract distillers is perhaps limited in this, the early period of the craft distilling movement, it will surely not always remain so. One lesson from the micro-brewing revolution lies in the way innovative and farsight-ed players in the supplies and services sector of the brewing industry, especially independent hop merchants such as Charles Faram, traditional floor maltsters such as Fawcetts, Warminster and others, and brewing engineers such as Murphy's, spotted the trend and adapted their services to exploit it. We would not have more than 1,000 micro-brewers in Britain today if these supply and service compa-nies had not evolved to fill the sector's needs. And surely the contract distillers are in a similar position; for not only do they actually distill, they also give their clients access to laboratory services, bottle designers, label designers, contract bottlers, bonded warehouses and all the other ancil-laries that start-ups would otherwise have to find for them-selves – in other words, by making their expertise available for hire contract distillers could save every newcomer the time, trouble, expense and opportunity for error of reinvent-ing the wheel. Langley has already taken a giant step in this direction as the key supplier of ethanol to craft gin rectifiers.

Not only that, but existing craft distillers can – and many of them probably will – develop busy sidelines as contrac-tors and consultants as well, as happened in the early days of microbrewing when pioneers like Peter Austin not only founded and ran their own breweries but also support-ed new entrants with a zeal that was as much evangelical as commercial. We have already seen Julian Temperley of Burrow Hill and Mike Hardingham of Ludlow casting themselves in the Peter Austin role; others with spare capacity and a thirst for cash-flow might well follow the same path. Indeed if craft distilling is to take off as microbrewing did all those years ago it must, to some extent, feed on its own success, which means that acolytes will seek gurus and gurus will – for a consideration – oblige.

## The processes of distillation

For most craft distillers, though, assembling and operating the nuts and bolts will be at least half of the fascination. They will want distilleries of their own.

### Alcoholic Liquor Duties Act 1979

Before we go into the processes of distillation, though, we need to consider ALDA 79 and HMRC's very limited powers to refuse a distiller's licence. Under ALDA section 12, no person may produce spirits unless they hold a distiller's licence from HMRC. ALDA section 12 used to provide HMRC with all sorts of discretionary reasons not to issue a licence (e.g. being near a brewery or vinegar maker etc.) All these provisions have since been revoked except for HMRC's discretionary power to refuse a distiller's licence in respect of premises in which the largest still is less than 18 hectolitres capacity, a throwback to the 1823 Excise Act when the minimum legal capacity was set at 40 gallons. A 40-gallon still, it was reasoned, was too big for a moonshiner to hide and too heavy to be thrown on to a cart and made off with should Excise officers suddenly appear. However as early as 1996 a new policy was established, following an appeal tribunal, that Customs needed a good reason to withhold permission for a still with a capacity of less than 18hl provided there were satisfactory controls in place to protect the revenue and the resources required to exercise those controls were not disproportionate. The same policy also allowed Customs to licence small stills for experimental use.

It took a good many years for this new policy to be universally adopted, but so many licences have been granted to distillers with small stills that provided you are a fit and proper with a genuine business case/need that you can demonstrate size should no longer matter.

## Liquor

Before you start distilling, you need a wash to fill your pot with. All spirits start life as fermented liquor of one sort or another – wine or wine lees, cider or perry, toddy, unhopped beer – and many craft distillers started life as producers of one or another of them. Indeed the movement started, as we never tire of saying, because two cidermakers foresaw an afterlife in the spirit world for their fermented liquors.

For most craft producers of gin and vodka, though, the drums (or one day, if all goes well, the 1,000-litre IBC) of neutral spirit from Langley or Haymans or elsewhere will always be a familiar part of the scenery. Neutral spirit is by no means cheap, but buying in saves a big investment in a hot liquor tank, a mash tun, fermenting vessels and a spirit still, as well as the space to put them in and the time and energy bills required to operate them; and as both Haymans and Langley are expert at what they do, why reinvent the wheel?

This dominance by white spirits will probably not last, though. The market is already awash with super-premium gins, and even though the scope for brand differentiation offered by the possible combinations of botanicals is almost infinite there are only so many bottles of £30–£50 gin that people are prepared to buy. More and more new entrants to the craft are likely to opt for a darker spirit, and for that they will mostly need to produce the fermented base themselves.

## World malt whisky shortage

There is a global shortage of whisky looming. The world's nouveaux riches – the Brazilians, the Russians, the Indians, the Chinese (or BRICs) – are drinking their way through the stuff so steadily that mature stocks of fillings are already running low; hence the appearance of premium "expressions" of top-shelf blends that carry no age statement. At time of writing something like 30 new malt distilleries, some of them enormous, as well as hefty extensions to existing sites are at various stages of development in Scotland itself; and many, many more are being built around the world. Whisky is also becoming a more and more important part of the English and Welsh craft distilling scene: Hicks & Healey, St Georges, and Penderyn are comparative veterans, and new whiskies are due from others including Cotswold, Lakeland, Ludlow and Chase. Given the explosion in world demand, it may very well be that the whole focus of the craft distilling boom switches from gin to whisky in the next few years.

And where there's a whisky there has to be a wash, which is essentially an unhopped ale of around 8–9% ABV. Hicks & Healey and Penderyn originally bought in their wash from St Austell and Brain's breweries respectively, although Penderyn has now installed its own brewhouse; the others brew their own, using kit that is both simple and comparatively inexpensive. But it's not only whisky that begins life as a mash of malt: even though many craft distillers base their products on cider or wine or even whey, brewing ale from grain is still the traditional starting-point for both gin and vodka.

## Malt

Brewing, of course, starts with malt, and you can buy it either ready-ground by the maltster or, for that true "grass to glass" credibility, invest in a malt-mill of your own. It's not a terribly expensive piece of kit, and having your own gives you that extra degree of control since you can use it to produce a grist of the fineness or coarseness that suits you best.

At time of writing, top-quality malt will cost you around £750 a tonne (although malt prices are quite volatile), which is enough to make 3,350-odd litres of wash at 8% ABV; and traditional floor maltsters such as Warminster are only too eager to broaden their customer base to include distillers. Distillers almost always opt for pale ale or even lager malts; the main variable as far as the flavour of the finished product concerned is the extent to which the malt has been peated, if at all. However a handful of distillers have conducted tentative experiments with different brewing malts, especially the biscuit brown and crystal varieties, with results that are... interesting.

## Mash tun and wash back

Next comes the hot liquor tank – a giant Burco, really – then the mash tun, in which you steep your grist in hot water to allow the diastase (the enzyme in malted barley) to convert the insoluble starches into maltose; and finally there's the fermenting vessel or, in whisky parlance, the wash back in which the wort, or malt syrup, is fermented with yeast. Larger and more sophisticated mash tuns come equipped with mechanised paddles and sparging arms to maximise the extraction of fermentable sugars from the malt; but our ancestors managed perfectly well without these refinements, and what we're really talking about is two big insulated buckets. (It's possible to get fantastic extractions on the simplest of kit simply by combining the mash tun and wash back and fermenting without straining the wort off the grist first. This is a very ancient technique still practised by some Bourbon distiller.) There is a superfluity of these vessels on the second-hand market, mainly from microbreweries that have outgrown their original plant;

and brewing consultants like Dave Porter (**www.pbcbrewery installations.com**), David Smith (**www.brewingservices. co.uk**) and a host of others can not only lay their hands on suitable vessels with ease, but will also come and install them for you.

## Boiler and other tanks

The same can be said of the boiler you will need if you plan to make ethanol from molasses, normally but not necessarily as a base for rum. Molasses needs to be watered down by a factor of three or four before fermentation, depending on how strong you want your base liquor to be; and molasses being the stubbornly gloopy stuff that it is this necessitates thorough boiling. Fortunately boilers (or "coppers" or "kettles") are a commonplace in the brewing industry, as hops need to be boiled in the sweet wort for 1½–2 hours to surrender their acids and aromatics, so there are plenty of cheap second-hand ones on the market – and even brand-new boilers aren't terribly expensive.

Other tankage you might need could include a blending or steeping vat, especially for fruit or herbal macerated liqueurs. This really is just a simple tank – an IBC would do the job perfectly well, as would any food-grade plastic vessel.

# The stills

One thinks of distillation as the art of separating liquids of different densities by evaporation. In truth, though, it might be better defined as the art of separating liquids of different densities by condensation, since it's not all that difficult to light a fire under a bucket of something, but damned tricky to recapture only the vapours one actually wants.

To illustrate the point, here's a description of possibly the least efficient still in the history of spirits, the ancient Chinese or Mongolian version. Imagine a three-tier open-work gantry standing over a low fire. On the lowest tier of the gantry is a wide copper bowl containing the liquor to be distilled. On the next tier up is a much narrower bowl or even a beaker, while on the top is another wide copper bowl filled with cold water or, even better, ice. The fire is just hot enough to evaporate the alcohol from the wine. The vapour condenses on the cold underside of the uppermost bowl, runs down it, and drips into the beaker (or, I suppose, spirit receiver) in the middle. You can immediately see the problem with this set-up: the condenser collects all the alcohols from the wine indiscriminately – those you want and those you don't; those that are wholesome, and those that will eventually kill you. The spirit might be perfectly suitable as a solvent for cosmetics, but not so good as a neutral base for beverages!

Before describing the two kinds of still in general use, it might be worth dispelling a widely-held myth. Freeze-distilling, or more accurately freeze-concentrating, is not considered to be distilling at all by HMRC – it's not illegal, it doesn't require any special kind of licence, anybody can do it and anybody can sell the resulting concentrated liquor.' physical here, just bear with me) that the nature of the liquor has been substantially altered by all that freezing and skimming, merely that it has been concentrated. Freeze-concentrating, however, is an unreliable method of distilling and not really a commercial proposition in the modern world (someone will now prove me wrong!); and duty will be charged according to the strength of whatever you eventually produce – so if it's over 22% ABV it will be charged as spirits.

There are, practically, two kinds of still in commercial use: the pot still that will process one batch of liquor at a time, and the column or continuous still that, as its name suggests, operates continuously. There are also vacuum stills, which employ pressure differentials rather than temperature differentials to separate liquids of different densities. They are often touted as more economical to run than heat-operated stills, but in fact it takes as much energy to run a vacuum pump as it does to heat a conventional still, and a vacuum still is much more prone to leaks and breakdowns. Broadly speaking, then (very broadly speaking, actually) the finer malt whiskies and Cognacs are produced in batches while purer but less characterful spirits such as grain whisky and the ethanol you might use as the foundation of your gin come from column stills.

One thing you will notice when browsing through catalogues of stills – indeed, one of the most visually attractive aspects of distilling – is the amount of copper on show. Copper isn't the distiller's metal of choice just because it looks good, though: it reacts with sulphides in the liquor that can cause off-flavours in the spirit, turning them into sulphates that pelletise and either precipitate harmlessly or adhere to the sides of the still and can be cleaned off with lemon juice.

## The pot still

The pot still seems to have been invented in the 8th or 9th century AD by Arabian chemists in Baghdad, principally as a bench-top retort used to produce solvents for the manufacture of medicines, lacquers and cosmetics. It had spread to Christendom via the great cosmopolitan medical school at Salerno by the late 11th century, but the spirits it produced were still used almost entirely as industrial and medical solvents until the 15th century.

The two-part copper stills that seem to have originated at about that time had a huge advantage over the simple laboratory retort: by changing the shape of the head, distillers could experiment with different condensation temperatures and thereby learn to manipulate the chemical composition of the eventual spirit. Big fat necks with large surface areas, they discovered, cooled more quickly and separated out much of the methanol and other impurities that condense at lower temperatures than ethanol, leaving a smoother (as well as a safer) spirit. On the other hand, extremely pure ethanol could be low in character, even bland.

Through long trial and error distillers all over Christendom learned what they and their customers wanted, and over a period of more than four centuries pot-still shapes and configurations evolved by rule of thumb. Reliable industrial thermometers weren't available until the 1750s and even then were slow to catch on which, given that a still is at bottom a heat-exchanger in which considerations such as the total surface area and thickness of the metal, the temperature within the still and the ambient temperature outside it are crucial, makes it all the more miraculous that any potable spirit was produced at all. Even today, while the principles are well understood, the variables are so many and complex that predicting how an individual still will perform and what it will produce is as much a matter of experience and intuition as of science. You will quickly come to know and even love your own pot-stills' quirks and foibles and you will, inevitably it seems, give them names.

## The column or continuous still

The continuous still in which grain whisky and most ethanol are made is an ingenious example of thermodynamic engineering dating from the 1820s. A number of pioneering variants were designed, but the first to produce a design practical enough to patent was an Irish excise officer, Aeneas Coffey, in 1830.

The Coffey still and its modern descendants comprise two towering columns of copper, the analyser and the rectifier. A continuous flow of wash circulates through the rectifier and then into the top of the analyser, while steam enters at the bottom of the analyser. The steam evaporates the alcohol out of the wash, and the whole cloud of mixed vapours rises to a funnel through which it is piped into the rectifier to be separated. And here's the clever bit: the continuous still recycles its own heat. The wash, fresh and cool from the fermenting vessel and on its way to the analyser, first passes through an immersion coil inside the rectifier, where it encounters the hot mixed vapour of water and alcohol on its way from the analyser. The wash therefore warms up while the steam, through contact with the wash, condenses at different temperatures into its constituent liquids, which are collected on plates and drained off separately as they do so. One of these separated liquids is ethanol, which is collected at 95.63 per cent pure. This is the azeotrope, the point at which further boiling will not remove any more of the water.

## The gin still

Gin is commonly made on what might loosely be described as a hybrid of the two, or rather a pot still with the rectifying column from a continuous still bolted on to it. The neutral spirit is watered down and redistilled in the pot still along with the botanicals, which are first steeped in hot spirit to loosen their aromatic oils and then either added directly to the still or hung in a bag in a bulbous appendage (the "carterhead") in the neck of the still. The former method gives a more robust gin; the latter, in which the volatiles are evaporated rather than boiled, a more refined one. The result is then passed through the rectifying column to separate out as much as possible of the heavier alcohols and other undesirable compounds. Other spirits can also be made on a gin still if a particularly smooth product is required.

## The Faraday or Penderyn still

Another ingenious hybrid is the still developed in the 1990s at the University of Surrey by a team headed by Dr David Faraday for the late Dafydd Gittins of Brecon Brewery. The story of Mr Gittins's rise and fall is well-known in the industry: in the 1970s, long before Bertram Bulmer and Julian Temperley arrived on the scene, he decided to revive the art of whisky distilling in Wales after a gap of a century or so. His first product was actually a vatted whisky malt filtered through Welsh-grown herbs and let down with Welsh spring water. Swn y Mor (the Sound of the Sea) was a commercial success – but what it wasn't was Welsh whisky – which is what he labelled it.

However, it took 18 years and the launch of a premium version, Prince of Wales, to sting the Scottish distillers into legal action against him, during which time Mr Gittins had raised a European research grant of €500,000 to fund the University of Surrey's research, had had the Faraday still made at McMillan of Prestonpans and had it installed at his base in Brecon. Before he could commission it, though, he was sued, lost the case and went out of business. Shortly afterwards the still was bought by Penderyn and moved to its HQ, where in 2000 Dr Faraday finally got to commission his brainchild. McMillan has recently constructed a second Faraday still, which has joined its older sibling on active service.

The Faraday still is, basically, a straightforward 25hl pot still with a seven-plate condensing column on top of it rather than the usual still head and lyne arm. Beside it stands an 18-plate rectifying column rather like a gin still, but what's really ingenious is the internal system of pumps that allows the vapour to be moved between plates, giving the master distiller absolute control over which fractions to retain and which to discard. It is also supremely efficient, producing 92 per cent pure spirit in a single pass, which saves a great deal of energy and creates a single malt whisky that is not only drinkable but excellent at only four years old. A slight downside is that the whisky it produces tends to be very light-bodied; Penderyn has therefore installed two conventional pot stills to create a richer, rounder malt. This can be overcome, however, by finishing in sherry or port casks – Penderyn itself has shown a fondness for Madeira casks. So far Penderyn is the only distillery to use the Faraday still, but it has great potential for its efficiency and economy and may well catch on with innovative craft distillers (subject, of course, to questions of intellectual property). McMillan would doubtless be glad if it did!

## Buying your still

One difference between the early days of the microbrewing boom and the current craft distilling revival is that small breweries were much cheaper and easier to equip. Not only could a skilled – or even, in some cases, a semi-skilled – fabricator cobble up a perfectly serviceable brewery from more or less any old vessels, but the failure rate in the early days was such that there was always plenty of second-hand kit floating about. Distilling equipment, on the other hand, is less easy to improvise. And although the first two English craft distilleries, King Offa and Somerset Royal, were kitted out with virtually antique stills sourced, appropriately enough, in Calvados country, there is far less second-hand distilling equipment on the market than there is brewing equipment. That means buying new – but where?

The British distilling industry is highly specialised and until recently has been very stable both in terms of the number of operators shopping for new equipment and of the kind of equipment they require. For the most part the established whisky and gin distillers have needed big vessels either to replace the old ones they already have or to equip the vast new super-distilleries they are frenziedly constructing. They also have long lead-in times: it's possible to predict when an elderly still will need replacing some years in advance, while the equipment for a big new plant can more or less be ordered off-plan and fabricated while the distillery buildings themselves are going up. In short, the market for new distilling equipment has until now been dominated by demand for big, costly, custom-built kit. By the same token, the discarded equipment put up for sale has tended to consist of large and expensive units. Not very helpful for the would-be craft distiller – although do have a sneaky look at the distilling and brewing page on **www.perryprocess.co.uk**, because you never know what you'll find!

## British manufacturers

The two big names in distillery equipment are Forsyths of Rothes in Banffshire and John Dore of Guildford, Surrey, and there are some surprising similarities between the two. Both were started when the foreman of an existing works bought out his employer: John Dore bought out the sons of Aeneas Coffey, developer of the column still, in 1872; while in 1933 Alexander Forsyth bought out the coppersmiths where he had worked for 40 years. Forsyth's is still run by the fourth generation of the family, but in a repeat of the process by which the Coffeys sold their London works to John Dore, the Dore family sold on to one of their directors, David Pym, in 1992. (McMillan of Prestonpans, **www.mcmillanltd.co.uk**, fabricator of the Faraday still described above, is another venerable name in still manufacture having been founded as Archibald McMillan in 1867 and still going strong.)

Spooky coincidences aside, the important question from our point of view is whether companies that execute vast projects all over the world can also design, build and install the equipment for much smaller distilleries. And indeed they can. Forsyths, for instance, built and installed the stills at the pioneering St George's whisky distillery in Norfolk, while the smallest pot-stills in the John Dore catalogue are a mere 500L. Nevertheless, the truth is that the enormous and sudden expansion of the distilling industry, not only in the UK but around the world, has led to a shortage of capacity in the supplying industries. If you approach one of the Big Two or McMillan Ltd direct they will undoubtedly do all they can to satisfy your needs, but you might find you're on a waiting list of anything up to three years.

## Distilling consultants and engineers

There are, however, intermediaries who will not only source all the equipment you need, design the processes and install the kit including pipework, pumps, tanks and all the rest of the paraphernalia but will also advise on thorny issues such as finance and HMRC compliance and will, pretty much, manage the entire project from empty shed to working distillery for you. The best-known engineering consultants are Allen Associates of Stirling. Alan Powell, formerly a senior official in HMCE's excise policy division, is among the top echelon of tax and compliance consultants and very kindly agreed to act as Consulting Editor on this book.

Allen Associates (**www.allenhpe.co.uk**) was founded in 1994 by chemical engineer Scott Allen and has worked with the biggest names in the Scotch whisky industry – Diageo, Chivas Brothers, Whyte & Mackay, William Grant & Sons – as well as smaller independents such as Gordon & Macphail, Ian McLeod and the newly-established Teeling distillery in Ireland. It has recently started working with an independent fabricator, Spey Projects Ltd, specifically to service the many craft distilleries that are clamouring for equipment.

The services of consultants/project managers such as don't come cheap, but unless you have vast experience yourself they are well worth the investment, not least because they can speed your way through the labyrinthine process of getting your HMRC licence. And not only will they design, equip and install for you a distillery that's HMRC-friendly, that's energy-efficient (important, that – your gas bill will be high) and that works, they'll build you one that's safe. Highly flammable spirits and spirit-vapour under pressure can explode if they're not rigorously controlled!

### Importing a still

Having said all that, there's no reason why you shouldn't build your distillery from scratch – plenty have. Provided you're a competent engineer – and provided you're credibly confident that you're a competent engineer! – you can source all the tankage, pipework, pumps, heat exchangers, and so forth that you need from the UK microbrewing supply industry while looking across the Channel for your actual still. All over Europe, wherever there's a vineyard, or a cider mill or a brewery, there's a distillery somewhere close by; and wherever there's a distillery there's a coppersmith manufacturing and maintaining its array of vessels. You could visit Galicia in Spain to inspect Hoga's catalogue (**www.hogacompany.com**) or head south to Portugal for a tour of the Iberian Coppers works (**www. copperalembic.com**). And while you might be in Bordeaux to sample the claret, you could also make a detour to Bègles on the outskirts of the city to look at the third-generation family firm Alambics Stupfler.

All of these companies – and dozens like them all over Belgium, the Netherlands, Scandinavia, Germany, Austria, Switzerland, Croatia, the Czech Republic, Slovakia, Poland and just about everywhere else where a tradition of small-scale distilling has survived – fabricate solid, high-quality, hand-crafted pot stills, columns, condensers and other equipment perfectly suited to the craft distiller. What they don't do is plan it, install it, plumb it in, and maintain it.

And although their prices look pretty good, you still have to ship your purchase back home.

# Ancillary equipment

The still may be the most important piece of equipment in the distillery (obviously!), but it requires a whole range of ancillary items to service it. Here are a few key pieces – your trainer or consultant will tell you the rest!

## Hydrometer or densimeter

At several points during the distillation process, you will be required to measure the alcoholic strength. The traditional method involves the trusty old hydrometer, "e" marked and conforming to British Standards Institute specification BS 718:1991; a thermometer, since all measurements have to be taken at $20^0$C; and the Practical Alcohol Tables Volume 2, on paper or online. More up-to-date methods are now permitted (see Sprit Regulations 3320 on the HMRC website), and larger distilleries generally possess an extremely sophisticated densimeter that does the job automatically. Densimeters, however, are expensive, and although the time-honoured way is a bit fiddly you'll quickly get the hang of it. An inexpensive hand-held refractometer, as used by home brewers and winemakers, is not a bad investment at this early stage: its measurements are not accepted as definitive by HMRC, but you can use it to check your hydrometer readings and make sure you're in the right ballpark.

## Bottling equipment

One of the irritants – one of the minor irritants, admittedly – of a profession like the author's that involves a lot of factory visits is that the piece of machinery that the management is proudest of and most eager to show off to visitors is the high-speed filling line. Whatever the product, be it mayonnaise or

# Case Study – Virtual Orchard
## www.virtualorchard.co.uk

If there was a competition to find the most artisanal of artisanal distillers, Laurence Conisbee would definitely be in the running for the big rosette.

Since 2009 Laurence has been making cider in a big barn in a former timber yard on a canal bank in Milton Keynes. The operation is called Virtual Orchard because Laurence doesn't actually have a real one. He uses apples from his garden, his friends' and neighbours' gardens, the 5,000 acres belonging to Milton Keynes Parks Trust (which includes a one-acre cider apple orchard), a small fruit farm in Northamptonshire and the kitchen gardens and orchards of various country houses in the surrounding district.

All of the fruit comes from within a 15 mile radius, and the vast majority of it is culinary and dessert, with a few crabs and wildings thrown in for good measure.

But it's Laurence's insistence on localism that has presented him with a problem. Part of it is that his canalside location, with a huge country park and caravan site, a towpath busy with ramblers, cyclists and commuters, and canal traffic including hire cruisers, private boats and even floating hotels all passing his doorstep, Virtual Orchards is doing tremendous business. Laurence makes and sells 35–40,000 litres a year and, quite early on in the proceedings, began to run out of sources of fruit.

"We could have redefined local as being a radius of 20 miles, but we didn't want to do that," he says. "A radius of 12–15 miles is traditionally the typical distance between market towns, which is a good definition of local; and besides, the region is filling up with small cidermakers and I didn't want to find myself competing with them for apples. So instead, I started thinking of extending the product range and apple brandy seemed a natural next step."

The first few tiny batches of Virtual Orchards English Apple Brandy were made at the English Spirit Distillery at Dullingham near Newmarket. In two years, 1,000 litres of Laurence's cider produced no more than 600 25cl and 50cl bottles, but in that time he learned two important things.

The first was that fully-matured cider, left to condition over the winter months, didn't make such good brandy as young, more acidic cider distilled as soon as the first fermentation was done. The second was that the cost of producing such small batches was too high: to make any kind of profit he had to sell almost the entire output direct from his shop, with only a few bottles sold at wholesale prices to a handful of favoured local outlets. If the brandy was to be commercial, he needed his own still.

And this is where the story becomes truly amazing. For in turning Virtual Orchard from a cider mill into a fully-functioning distillery Laurence spent not the £100,000 recommended by one consultant as the absolute minimum, nor even the £50,000 invested by Ludlow Vineyard, but £3,500! Yes, that's right – £3,500! How?!

Well, that was what he paid for a 300-litre direct-fired pot still from Portugal complete with old-school worm-tub condenser and a gas-powered burner that turned out, on arrival, to be nothing more sophisticated than a standard paella stove. "An everyday piece of garden equipment over there, but not so common over here," he says.

Of course, Laurence cheated to an extent in that he wasn't starting from anything like scratch: he was already making and bottling cider and was already selling contract-made apple brandy, which kept the capital costs right down and meant he didn't need a substantial float. And the new apparatus didn't take all that much installing, either. All the same, an outlay that small puts artisanal distilling within everyone's reach, doesn't it?

Laurence still had the inevitable wrestling-match with HMRC to go through, though – but with a little ingenuity and foresight he managed to keep the pain of that down to a minimum, too. Having worked with English Spirit, and as a fairly near neighbour of Warner Edwards, he'd heard what they'd been through in their own licence applications; so when he applied on his own behalf he took the precaution of attaching a lengthy supporting document setting out everything he thought HMRC would want to know.

"There isn't really an application form as such," he says. "They just want information: what you plan to distill, what you're going to distill it on, whether there's a credible market for it – everything, really. So knowing what questions they were likely to ask I prepared as much information as I could in advance, and that smoothed the process considerably."

There were hitches, of course: HMRC likes to do business by snail mail, so when Laurence emailed a blueprint he was asked to post two more copies. "When I pointed out that they could just print off two more copies they actually apologised," he says. They also wanted to inspect the still before approving it, but Laurence didn't want to pay for the still until it had been approved. It could have been a stand-off, but in the end HMRC compromised and gave him strictly provisional and unofficial approval based on photographs and diagrams.

"In general they were pretty helpful, and the hitches were mainly down to procedure," he says. "They certainly seem perfectly used to the idea that a spirit still doesn't need to be 18HL in capacity – they looked at my business plan and they could see how much apple brandy I'd actually sold and they readily agreed that an 18HL still would be absurd."

Like a true artisan, Laurence was also careful not to confine his licence application to what will be his main product, apple brandy. He wants to keep his business flexible enough to be able to exploit whatever opportunities arise in his neighbourhood.

"Local people already bring me their surplus apples to press but I know that there's all sorts of unwanted fruit growing round here – soft fruit, top fruit, stone fruit, you name it. It would all make good eau-de-vie." As a result Laurence's distillery – christened Wharf after its canalside home – has become a real local institution. Its 300L pot still, Velocity, has produced malt spirit for local microbreweries as well as Laurence's own apple brandy, rum and whisky (new make should be available soon). Now he's crowdfunding for a second and one of the spirits he's like to make has an unusual source – cows.

"There's a dairy farmer here who makes cheese and at the moment has to dispose of all the leftover whey," he says. "Whey's full of lactose. You can ferment it. And if you can ferment it, you can distil it."

malt whisky, and whatever the receptacle, be it jam-jar or jeroboam, you can be sure that the filling line is everybody's favourite toy. And not entirely without reason: most manufacturing processes are fairly low on spectacle, and the blurring speed at which a modern filling line operates can be, until one tires of it, almost close to awe-inspiring.

There is no such excitement on the bottling line of a craft distillery, nor indeed on the filling line of any small processing plant where the work has to be done mainly by hand. One microbrewer of the author's acquaintance even gave up bottling altogether, not because there was no demand for his beer in bottled format but simply because he couldn't stand the tedium any more. Fortunately, distilling has a double advantage over brewing in this respect: spirits come in larger bottles than beer and are a much higher-value, lower-volume product: on both counts the number of bottles to be filled is generally much smaller and the time spent doing it commensurately shorter. A simple (and fairly inexpensive) four-head Vigo filler (**www.vigopresses.co.uk**) should manage 500 70cl, 50cl or 37.5cl bottles an hour, although the hour will be a fairly intensive one. (Miniatures for promotional and tasting purposes you will almost certainly have to fill entirely, and very carefully, by hand!)

## Achieving closure

Actually filling the bottles is only the half of it though. First you have to rinse them thoroughly, an operation for which a variety of mechanical aids from the simple (and, again, fairly inexpensive) to the fully-automated is available from firms such as Vigo Ltd; then you have to drain them upside down either on a special draining tree or simply in a plastic crate. Then, once the bottles are full, you have to cap them. Most spirits bottles are closed with aluminium tamper-evident screw-caps that come as blanks and require an (expensive) machine to mould them to the screw-thread on the bottle. They don't look very classy though, and a better (and much cheaper) alternative is to use sherry-style cork stoppers instead, inserted manually. A stopper, though, is not tamper-evident, so you need either to dress it with a simple paper seal; apply a capsule, which has to be foil, not plastic, and requires yet another expensive machine to apply; or simply dip the neck in hot sealing wax, which looks good and might even dribble appealingly down the side of the bottle as it dries.

Then, of course, you'll want a nice label or preferably labels. You'll almost certainly want a back label or neck label or both as well as the front label, and given that you have to include the official duty-paid stamp in your bottle-dressing, you'll probably need at least a back label to accommodate it. Get self-adhesive: nobody wants to mess around with glue unless they have to. If your bottles are round, as most whisky and brandy bottles are, you can get a very inexpensive manual device that rolls the label accurately on to the bottle; if your bottles are square, as gin bottles tend to be – well, an automatic labelling machine is a hugely expensive indulgence. That means applying the labels by hand and eye; and if no two bottles are quite the same, that's all part of the charm.

## Waste disposal

An important step in the brewing process is getting rid, safely and hygienically, of the vast amounts of water you will use. This water is going to be full of all sorts of pollutants, some of them organic – bits of malt grist, protein, suspended solids – and some of them chemical; in particular, industrial-strength detergents, because your vessels and pipework will get terribly sticky and will require frequent and thorough cleaning. The waste water may also have an undesirably low pH value.

You can't simply flush it down the drain – not, at any rate, without Trade Effluent Consent from your water and sewerage provider. This comes with a detailed question-naire about what sort of and how much effluent you propose to discharge; the best advice is to be scrupulously honest, since if you breach the terms of your consent the sewerage provider not only can but probably will revoke it altogether (it can fine you, too). And since sewerage providers continu-ally monitor discharges, you won't get away unnoticed with craftily tipping it away, either. Especially as it's likely to be hundreds of thousands of gallons a year!

Alternative methods of disposing of waste water are reed beds and French-style sand traps, for either of which you will need Discharge Consent from the Environment Agency.

Reed beds are less popular as an environmentally friend-ly way of disposing of pollutants than they used to be. The right reeds can and will actually digest most if not all of the nasties you will generate, and the site itself will be a haven for wildlife. But there are drawbacks: you may not have enough space, and establishing a reed bed is a slow and expensive process. Two sites where you'll find more information about reed-beds are **www.oceans-esu.com** and **www.sheepdrove.com**.

The sand trap is used by the millions of French rural homes that are not connected to mains drainage to purify the really nasty waste water from baths, showers, washing machines, dishwashers and, of course, lavatories. Foul water from the septic tank is discharged via a perforated hosepipe through a big, metre-deep and preferably sloping sand-pit. The sand itself filters out trace minerals such as copper, while colonies of sludge-eating bacteria rapidly build up to deal with the organic components. These sand-traps are clean, safe, easy to dig, almost maintenance-free and above all cheap; but while the French pretty much take them for granted they are almost unknown in the UK.

For more details on effluent discharge regulations either visit the Environment Agency website or call its helpline, 03708 506506.

## Draff and pot ale

If you make your own wash you will, through the course of a year, have to dispose of tonnes and tonnes of what the Scottish call "draff" – a soggy mass of spent malt, apple pomace or grape pulp. Although most of the sugars should have been extracted from it, it still makes a highly nutritious animal feed on which Scottish cattle and pigs have been happily snacking for generations. Since the various outbreaks of livestock infections of the 1990s, though, the whole business has been regulated and you now need to register with the Brewing, Food & Beverage Industry Suppliers Association's Feed Assurance Scheme – which involves passing a training course and paying a fee – before you can sell your draff to local farmers. It's worth it, though: the trickle of cash-flow it generates will quite possibly be the first money you actually lay hands on. Visit **www.bfbi.org.uk** for more details.

Pot ale is a different matter altogether. You'll make ten times as much pot ale as you do spirit, because it's the liquid left in your still after the alcohols have evaporated. And it can't be poured down the drain, even with Trade Effluent Consent: its rich mixture of spent yeast, carbohydrates, proteins and minerals makes it a heaven on earth for microbes of all descriptions, and it needs to be treated by a specialist firm before disposal. It can be boiled down to a thick tasty sludge that cattle love, especially when mixed up with the draff.

Tullibardine and Celtic Renewables Ltd of Edinburgh have designed a bacterial process that turns pot ale into biofuel, and other big distillers are working on other ways of recycling it. For most craft distillers, though, the local effluent disposal contractor is the most practical resort.

# 06

# Finance and Compliance

You could spend a fortune on building and equipping your distillery, and indeed many people do. But you don't have to. The specialised nature, the availability and the sheer quantity of the equipment you will need make a distillery start-up, even a modest one, more expensive than a brewery start-up but still very much less expensive (and hopefully far more profitable) than, say, buying a pub. So assuming your ambitions don't extend to challenging Bell's or Gordons for the nation's number one best-seller slot, just how much capital should you reasonably expect to have to find? Or, since the sky is really the limit, a more sensible question might be: how little can you get away with? One distilling consultant puts the bare minimum outlay on equipment at £100,000, and one of the many new start-up Scotch malt whisky distilleries has reputedly invested £250,000. But could you get away with less?

## Premises

For some classes of business, finding a site is the most expensive item on the shopping list. In high-class retail, for instance, the premium for a lease in a suitable location might come to more than the cost of the fittings and the stock combined. The same could be said of the hotel and pub trades. A distillery, however, is a factory and is perfectly at home on an industrial estate. And the less prestigious the home the better, in some ways: not only will its modesty be reflected in both the premium (if there is one) and the rent, it should also have a commensurately low rateable value – and if the rateable value is under £12,000, you could get a 50 per cent rebate on your business rates. If the RV is less than £6,000, you should get an initial period free of business rates altogether.

Alternatively, you might be a winemaker, a cidermaker, a farmer or the owner of a heritage property and already have a building earmarked for your still. In which case, register your distillery as a company in its own right, get the building which will house it separately valued for business rates, lease the building to the distillery company and see if, as a result, it qualifies for relief. It might also qualify for one of the dwindling number of government grants on offer to start-ups: the Agri-Tech Growth Initiative Grant for new products or ideas that improve agricultural productivity; a grant for start-ups in deprived area; a grant for repairs to historic building, which would at least help with the conversion. Visit **www.gov.uk/business-finance-support-finder** to discover just how little support there is these days.

Other than that, all your building requires (apart from planning permission, that is!) is mains services – including gas, which is the cheapest fuel for heating your still's steam coils – washable floors and walls, preferably concrete, and as much space as you can afford.

## Capex

How much will your distillery cost to buy and install? Well, as much as you like. The sky really is the limit, so perhaps the best way to arrive at an estimate is to start with the most basic distillery imaginable; you can scale up from there according to your ambitions and your resources.

The £100,000 quoted above was estimated as the barest possible minimum required to equip a small whisky distillery, which of course needs the best part of a brewery: a hot liquor tank, a malt mill, a mash tun (preferably with sparging arm, although a mechanised paddle might perhaps be something of an unjustifiable indulgence) and a fermenting vessel or wash back. None of these items are necessarily expensive, but it all adds up. Allow perhaps £10,000 for the brewing equipment; less if you are able to find it second-hand (not actually all that easy, since when a brewery expands it tends to sell its old kit as a single lot, and you don't need a complete brewery because you're not going to boil your fermented wash with hops). A gin or vodka plant would, of course, be that much cheaper in terms of capital expenditure, since it will need neither brewery nor spirit still.

## Imported stills

As for the stills, you can import either a pair of beautiful copper 500L pot stills or a pot still with a small rectifying column to go with it from Germany or Spain or Portugal for around €20,000 all told that – when you convert it into sterling but then add the VAT – comes rather neatly to about £20,000. (Having said that, Virtual Orchard of Milton Keynes sourced a 250L still from Portugal for a mere £3,500 – but its circumstances are rather unusual.) Add to this, though, the cost of carriage and a formidable list of accessories including a steam generator and heating coils or jacket, a condenser, a spirit safe, a spirit receiver and sufficient oak casks in which to mature your whisky or apple brandy and you can easily double it. Then there's the bottle-filler and its associated bits and pieces and all the pumps and pipes to connect it all up; the labour to install it all; the label and website designers' fees; office furniture and equipment; enough raw materials and bottles to see you through until the sales start coming in; a cash float for overheads such as rent, wages and utilities... suddenly an outlay of £100,000 is beginning to look conservative. A budget twice the size would get you bigger and better equipment; a budget thrice the size would get the whole plant professionally designed and installed, too.

## Gross profit

Having invested £100,000–£300,000, your next consideration, naturally enough, is going to be what sort of return you can reasonably expect.

First, we need some idea of how much spirit such a rock-bottom 500-litre rig might actually produce. Let's start with gin (and vodka). Filling your still with 200 litres of bought-in ethanol and 300 litres of water should yield up to 700 70cl bottles of 40% ABV spirit, depending on the efficiency of your set-up. (It could be rather less, but the magic number here is 28 – that is, a 70cl bottle of 40 % ABV spirit contains 28clpa). If, on the other hand, you are producing your own wash from malt or fruit or pressed grape-pulp, then 500 litres of it at 8–9% ABV will yield only about 50 litres of pure alcohol – less, once the feints have been discarded; enough to fill 170-odd 70cl bottles at 40% ABV.

Not only will it take you eight runs (12, if you triple-distill) to produce as much whisky as a single run will produce gin, the ingredients could also cost you more than twice as much. One leading supplier of ethanol charges in the region of £1,135 plus delivery per 1,000l, or £2,490 if you choose to go organic; so it will cost you at least £225 to charge your still and end up with 700 bottles. If you brew your own wash, aiming for around 9% ABV, it will take 180kg of malt at about £700–£750 a tonne (a figure that will fluctuate depending on the harvest and how important a customer you are) to brew 500l; so, about £120 per mash and therefore £480–600 to end up with the same number of bottles as your gin-rectifying opposite number. (And it'll take up to 12 times as much fuel as well, although you will, naturally – and it's surprising how many businesses don't do this – be buying your utilities on industrial tariffs.) But at 35p a bottle for gin and vodka and 70–80p for whisky (but nothing at all if you're distilling cider from your own apples or grappa from your pressed grape pulp and bottle rackings), the raw materials turn out to be among the least expensive items on your list of overheads. And in fact the distiller making whisky or brandy from scratch does enjoy one significant advantage over most of the smaller gin rectifiers or vodka redistillers, which is that unless the producers of white spirits possess a fully-bonded warehouse they will generally have to pay the duty – £28.74 a litre (as of 2017) – to whoever sells them their ethanol before delivery, whereas distillers from scratch can mature their product in duty suspension until it's ready for sale. So that's £5,750 the rectifier has to find upfront that the distiller doesn't.

## Wholesale pricing

Next, what will it fetch? Craft-distilled spirits have settled quite comfortably into the same price-bracket as Cognac and single malt whiskies – i.e., from the upper twenties to an as yet untested infinity – that is a better premium than even the most highly-regarded mainstream gins used to command. But let's be modest and take £30 as a retail price. Of that, a minimum of £8.04 goes straight to the Treasury in the form of duty, whose rate at time of writing is £28.74 per litre of pure alcohol. What happens to the remaining amount depends on who you sell the bottle to. Sell it direct to a customer online and you get to keep the lot, which is one of the joys of internet trading. If, on the other hand, you sell your bottle to a wholesaler or a wine merchant you might expect to retain half to two-thirds of it – say £13 net of ingredients and duty.

A gross profit of £13–£22 per unit, depending on sales channel, is not at all bad, but how much of that you get to keep depends on your overheads, which will fluctuate dramatically from business to business depending on variables such as your rent, your wage-bill, your utilities, your loan repayments and the cost of disposing of your pot ale. It is not possible in a book like this to make an account of all those outgoings – that's something you will have to do for yourself when writing your business plan. But at least you now have a sound idea of roughly how much GP will be available to meet them, and how much of it will be left over as net profit after they've all been paid.

## Cash flow

A century or so ago it was decreed that whisky couldn't call itself whisky until it had spent at least three years in oak barrels. This is now one of the whisky industry's proudest boasts, although at the time it was actually a consumer protection measure. But although the compulsory aging of whisky – which must mature in cask for even longer than Cognac – is now seen as a badge of quality rather akin to the German Reinheitsgebot that prevents the adulteration of beer, it also puts something of a brake on cash-flow. Gin, vodka and the various eau-de-vie can start earning their keep the moment they're bottled; but whisky – and for that matter apple brandy – take time. A start-up manufacturing company facing a minimum of three years (and, in practice, much longer than that, because who could sell such a raw young spirit at any sort of premium?) without earning a penny is pretty much a no-no for any sane banker or investor. But there are ways round it.

The first thing to notice is that only a handful of the 50–60 new distilleries that have appeared since the beginning of the century produce only whisky. Many of them, especially but not only the Scottish newcomers, see themselves primarily as whisky distillers, but that hasn't deterred them from diversifying into white spirits that don't need to be matured and can be sold the moment they're filled into bottles. Interestingly, this takes us right back to the 17th century and the moment when gin and whisky diverged from their common ancestor. Both started out as identical distillates of malted barley, but the big landowners of eastern England poured capital into huge industrial distilleries and went for a rapid turn-round on their investment by flavouring and rectifying the raw spirit for instant sale, while the small farmers of the Scottish uplands saw distilling as a way of maintaining the price of the surplus produce of good harvests: they stored their spirit in oak and released it on to the market a little at a time. The same thing is happening again today, but in reverse: small-scale distillers are turning to white spirits to guarantee them a reasonable cash-flow, while only the bigger distillers have the capital to concentrate solely on stocks of whisky or brandy that take years to mature before they are saleable.

Diversifying into gin rectification to generate some cash-flow has become something of a commonplace, but it does have a significant implication that needs to be taken into account. Any product that has your brand name on it has to be top-quality, and not just a sideline. The formulation of a unique and alluring grist of botanicals is an art that needs great care and expertise. And the gin has to be market-ed energetically, or the promise of cash generation will remain just that... a promise. In short, you'll be running two product lines at the same time, which is fine if you're prepared for it – and plenty of people do it, after all – but potentially disastrous if you're not. It's not purely a matter of focus, either: it's also a matter of resources. It takes enough time, energy and money to run a single business: are you sure you have the time, energy and money to run two, which is effectively what you'll be doing?

## Selling new make

There are, however, two fairly well-trodden paths for whisky and brandy distillers seeking to generate cash flow while their stocks slumber in bond. The first and easiest way is to bottle and sell limited quantities of new make not as whisky or brandy but as eau-de-vie. This is an option with all sorts of advantages. The first is that true aficionados are always eager for something new, and the very existence of your eau-de-vie will be enough to persuade some people to buy it. The second is that it complements, rather than detracts from, the marketing of your principle product. It becomes a forerunner, a countdown to the main event, a John the Baptist to... well, that's enough of that. Suffice it to say that it will create anticipation, even suspense, and build a market for your single malt whisky even before it is released. The third is that a bottle of craft-made eau-de-vie or hors d'age, though immature, can command the same price as the whisky it will one day become. You can ring the changes with it, too, macerating Williams pears or Mirabelle plums to create special editions that will keep your growing army of fans enthused and enthralled. Of course, you won't sell a huge amount in terms of numbers of bottles, but the very rarity value keeps the retail price high.

## Selling stock in bond

The second method used to be regarded as very unreliable, and indeed many of the unwary got stung by the unscrupulous before the practice all but died out. But it has now been rediscovered, and with an added ingredient: honesty.

This is the practice of selling maturing stocks in bond to investors long before it is ready for bottling, and once upon a time it was a notorious con. People who'd been promised dizzyingly huge profits on cellars stuffed with fine clarets or chock-a-block with fabulous ports found either that the stocks didn't exist at all or, if they did, that they were miserable stuff only fit to make antifreeze out of.

The trick here is to build up a personal relationship of trust and even friendship with the putative owners of your maturing stocks. You can either sell them a whole cask of their very own, with their name stamped on it, which they can pop along from time to time to visit, to pat, to stroke and to take an investigative sip from, and which you will, when the time is exactly right, bottle for them; or they might buy a share in a particular make and draw a profit from its eventual sale. Either way, you should try to limit this sort of sale to customers who know their whisky; you should encourage them to visit and take an interest; and you should explain that their investment is fun money and that they shouldn't expect more than an average return on it. In this way you will develop a reputation for honesty and straight dealing of inestimable value. In the long term you might actually lose money on this kind of trade because you will be selling your output, or a part of it, for less than it will eventually be worth. But you'll only sell a predetermined and affordable proportion of your stock to these investors, and if the income from it goes not only towards your running overheads but also to debt reduction it will be well worth it. It's exactly how Cotswold Distillery is funding the construction of its own bonded warehouse, which in time will save the whole cost of transporting its stock to Liverpool and paying rent for having it matured in bond there. (It helps that the founder is an old City hand with a network of contacts among whom the £2.5 million he wants to raise is, if not pocket money, not an impossible dream either.)

In the meantime, you are also helping to market your brand by establishing a committed following – a family, even – of customers who are knowledgeable, enthusiastic and of necessity fairly well-heeled. This is not just good for your cash flow: it's word-of-mouth generation at its very finest.

## Accounting and paying duty and VAT

Excise duty will undoubtedly be your single biggest bill, and it's the one bill you can't ignore or put off. How do you do it?

Remembering that spirits have to be put into excise warehouse immediately following collection in the spirits vat/distiller's warehouse, the duty has to be accounted for under the warehousing regulations when the goods are released for consumption (EWER section 16(4), since you ask.) The way HMRC has arranged the procedure is as follows: the warehousekeeper (you, in this case) has to "enter" the goods for removal from the warehouse and pay the duty on them before they are physically removed. The "entry" is actually achieved by filling in warrant W5 and submitting it to HMRC together with payment. The goods can't be released until HMRC confirms payment has been made, which is a pain. However, you can submit the W5 online and make a BACS payment, allowing you to release the goods immediately. Never be tempted to by-pass this arrangement – you will break the law and can be heavily penalised, and even have your approval revoked. If the goods are your own (which they should be), there is no VAT to account for on the W5 warrant.

It's also possible to account for the duty on goods removed from the warehouse for consumption on a "daily" warrant; but instead of making immediate payment, you can be approved by HMRC to defer the duty. Under this arrangement, HMRC keeps a running total of your daily deferment entries (using form W5D instead of W5) and debits what you owe at the end of the accounting period. This gives a deferment trader an average credit period of 28 days as well as being simpler to administer. The catch is in the standard deferment conditions imposed by HMRC that (a) you have sufficient funds to pay what you owe (fair enough!) and (b) that you provide a guarantee for the full duty liability in the period. You need a guarantor (i.e. your bank) to agree to this with HMRC, so the bank will want you to indemnify it before agreeing to be the guarantor. It gets worse because the terms of the guarantee are that HMRC can call upon the guarantor to pay up to twice the monthly deferred amount (because the accounting period actually straddles two months). So the bank has a 200 per cent exposure of your monthly liabilities and will want indemnity from you for the lot before signing up as guarantor! Little wonder few new distillers take this up. The procedures involved in applying for and operating under the duty deferment scheme are set out in HMRC Notice 101 and Notice 197 Chapter 11.5.

There is, however, one option that can be helpful. Under the Excise Payment and Securities System (EPSS), HMRC will allow a deferment trader to operate with nil security (i.e. no guarantee) if the applicant has a three-year VAT record with good compliance and sufficient liquidity of assets to meet any deferred payment of excise duty. This was a hard-won concession – it took three years before HMRC and the Treasury acquiesced and set up the EPSS scheme in 2007, so use it if you can!

## Methods of payment

You can pay your duty bill by one of several methods: cash (which might raise a few eyebrows in these days of money-laundering regulations); a banker's draft; a cheque covered by the bank's standard guarantee; a cheque endorsed by your bank manager (bit old-fashioned, this); or, to be up to the minute, and provided your monthly bill is – as it probably will be – less than £20,000,000, BACS. Unfortunately HMRC won't accept payment via your company credit card. But don't let that put you off using it!

## The company credit card

Of course, all the duty that goes out comes back in again soon enough, but if you are allowing trade customers 30 days' credit or more, as you may find yourself forced to do sometimes, it could pose something of a cash-flow problem – at least in the early phase of your business or when times are leaner than usual. This where the company credit card comes in.

It's surprising that more traders don't exploit the interest-free credit period of up to six weeks they can get by judicious use of their company credit card. It's so simple it feels like a scam, but in reality it's just a sensible piece of financial discipline. If you pay for all your consumables – malt, ethanol, bottles, labels and so on – by credit card on or immediately after the day you receive your monthly credit card statement, it will appear a month later on your next statement and you'll be given a fortnight or three weeks to pay. If you always pay in full – and just make sure that you do! – then hey presto, you've got six–seven weeks' interest-free credit! But this is something not only you should make a regular practice of. Encourage your trade customers to pay you by company credit card, too – insist on it, even: that way you get your money, including the duty element, within a couple of days of the transaction, while (thanks to you) your customers also get the benefit of six weeks' interest-free credit.

## Duty-paid stamps

Since 2006 it's been compulsory to display a duty-paid stamp on every bottle of alcohol of 30% ABV or more (and 37.5cl or more) sold in the UK.

The stamp, a dark red roundel 25mm across with a fluorescent patch that shows up yellow under UV light, can either be applied separately or can be incorporated into your label. Each one bears your own number preceded by an identifying letter saying what's in the bottle – 'W' for whisky, 'G' for gin, 'R' for rum and so on. To register for the stamps you can fill in form DS1 online at **www.hmrc.gov.uk** or download a paper version and post it to the NRU. Once you're registered, you can order either a stock of separate stamps or a CD-Rom that will allow your label-printer to incorporate your stamp into your bottle-labels.

It's a fairly simple process – and it's free! – but it has proved surprisingly effective in curbing bootlegging (although, perhaps, not quite as effective as the 10-year freeze in duty did). All you have to do, really, is let HMRC know if any of your stamped labels are lost, stolen or damaged. (The regulations affecting separate or "freestanding" stamps are more complicated, but these are really intended for importers and therefore won't concern you.)

The fine, incidentally, for selling your goods without a duty-paid stamp is £250. Per bottle!

## Alcohol Wholesaler Registration Scheme

Before you finally get started, you'll also have to sign up with HMRC's new Alcohol Wholesaler Registration Scheme, another piece of bureaucratic entanglement that is supposed to stop duty fraud by establishing a digital paper-trail of wholesale transactions in alcohol. You can register online by going to the New User's Registration Page on HMRC's website, where you will be issued with a Government Gateway ID and password. There's no charge but since the process takes time you need to remember to apply at least 45 working days before you start trading. Full details of AWRS can be found in Excise Notice 2002 s3.

# 07

# The Hard Sell

It has been said – probably by somebody in sales and marketing – that while any department can cause a company to fail, only sales and marketing can cause it to succeed. The most important people in any company, therefore, are its sales and marketing team. Beacuse you can make the worst product in the world, but given the right position in the market and a good sales rep it'll sell. Conversely, you can make the best product in the world but if your sales and marketing aren't up to snuff it'll squat there in the warehouse while you go slowly broke. The likelihood here is that unless you're unusually well-capitalised you're going to be your own sales department, so if you hadn't reckoned on spending more time out there selling your product than you do actually making it, now might be the right time for a rethink.

But you shouldn't let the prospect put you off. The marketing side should be largely a matter of instinct: you know your product inside out, so you'll have a strong idea of the appropriate demographic and price-point, and your bottle and label designers will ensure that the packaging and dressing accurately express the character and values of your brand. And selling, provided you have the resilience to soak up and even learn from the inevitable rejections, can become one of the most satisfying parts of the job. Repeat customers soon become good friends who look forward to seeing you, and because what you're selling is something you've thought up and brought to life yourself, every sale is a personal vindication.

Before we plunge into the world of sales and marketing, though, there's one time-consuming chore that will help enormously in selling your product that you might as well get out of the way well before you're ready to start trading: getting a personal liquor licence.

## Personal licences

The Licensing Act 2003 that came into force in November 2005 took the liquor licensing function away from the local magistrates and awarded it instead to district and borough councils. What this means, in practice, is much wider and more detailed consultation than in the old days, which is something we shall go into a little later on. The important provision of the Act for our present purposes was to split liquor licences in two, so you now have to have separate personal and premises licences (which we'll come to later). Ill-informed critics at the time claimed this merely added another layer of bureaucracy to an already growing pile; in fact, it did away with the cumbersome system of Transfer Sessions and Protection Orders and made it much easier for licensees to migrate between premises.

But it also meant that you could hold a personal licence without owning or operating a licensed premises, which is why you must have one. Possession of a personal licence allows you hold up to 12 open days a year on your premises by submitting an application for a Temporary Events Notice, and to retail liquor on other occasions such as farmers' markets (although be sure to check the venue has a premises licence – many of them don't!). You can hold the licence for a third-party's event, too – an agricultural show or community event, for instance, where you might just want to set up a stall to show off (and sell) your wares.

## Compulsory training

The personal licence is issued by your local council for a nominal fee. Before you apply, though, you'll need a National Certificate for Personal Licence Holders, and to get one of those you need to attend a one-day training course which has a 40-question multiple choice exam at the end. This will cost about £400. The British Institute of Innkeeping accredits some 500 training providers who run courses at over 5,000 locations all over the country – to find one, visit **www.biiab. org**. The sheer number of training providers means you can shop around for the cheapest, but before enrolling do make sure that they actually teach the one-day course as well as the five-day National Certificate in Licensed Retailing course. Not all of them do. To gain a personal licence you will also need a Disclosure and Barring Service check. Your local authority's liquor licensing department should give you an application form before you apply for the licence itself.

It's important to note that a personal licence alone does not allow you to sell liquor online, but the virtue of getting a personal licence under your belt fairly early on is that once it's done it's done. You can apply for a premises licence when you start trading – and you will need one before you begin internet trading – secure in the knowledge that at least one hoop has been jumped through.

## Marketing and publicity

Marketing might be defined as the thought processes that go into the actual selling. We have already touched on the question of demographics, and the price-point will more or less set itself once you've done your sums. But there are other questions to consider, the first one being brand identity – in particular, what your bottle and label are going to look like. This is important, because it will beget the branding for all the rest of your publicity material and if it's not right, or if you're not happy with it, then you're stuck with it.

If your professional background means you're familiar with commercial design this won't be a problem; if you're not, your first step is to take a good, hard and above all critical look at other products aimed at the same demographic as yours. That's not to suggest that you should simply imitate a design you think is effective – quite the contrary, in fact. Your bottle may never have to compete for attention with others on the supermarket shelves, but it will hopefully be distributed online by internet traders such as Beers of Europe (**www.beersofeurope.co.uk**), Flaviar (**www.flaviar.**

com) and Master of Malt (**www.masterofmalt.com**) and via the websites of any independent wine merchants who will stock your brand. In one important sense all these sites are – virtually, of course – the same as supermarket shelves. Shoppers in both cases have only visual clues to go on, so your branding is critical in influencing their decisions. Once you've chosen a designer, therefore, make sure you have a detailed brief prepared; talk it through thoroughly and don't settle for anything that you feel doesn't live up to your ideal. (Most bottle designers and suppliers are members of the British Bottlers' Institute – visit **www.bbi.org.uk**– others are listed in the Directory of Suppliers at the back of this book.)

## Your website

The same is true of your own website. Website designers, especially younger ones, have a tendency to put the medium before the message and use every tool in their electronic box, and while a site that's all movement and lights may be ideal for promoting a hip, edgy, cutting-edge gin or vodka aimed at the IT-savvy, the whisky demographic by and large is more attracted by something more understated and sedate – and, given that traditionalists tend to be older and less computer-literate, easy to navigate.

All in all it's better, if more expensive, to hire a professional web designer with an understanding of marketing rather than allow an enthusiastic nephew to do it for peanuts. And even if you yourself are not an internet junkie – especially if you yourself are not an internet junkie! – don't let yourself be bullied. If you aren't attracted by the site and find it difficult to use and even a bit intimidating, chances are your customers won't like it either.

# Publicity and promotion

Deciding where your brand belongs and dressing it appropriately is the first half of marketing. The second, and much more difficult, half lies in communicating its existence and its values.

## Advertising and sponsorship

The first thing to do here is: forget about advertising and sponsorship. Or, to qualify that, forget about advertising and sponsorship as methods of building your brand. Brand-building through advertising and sponsorship is hideously expensive and really only suitable for mass-market brands.

You might look at small-scale and very tightly controlled sponsorships, particularly of local events that have an appeal to your demographic – country and equestrian sports such as clay-pigeon shoots, point-to-point races or three-day events, say – which you would support with advertising in the brochure and possibly the local press – but sponsorships need a lot of work to be effective. You have to be on parade in person and you need a stall where your brand and its accompanying merchandise are on sale to recoup your outlay.

But as far as advertising goes, well – there are precious few suitable print titles to advertise in. Wine and beer lovers have their media, but other than *Whisky Magazine* and *Gin Magazine* and occasional features in food and drink magazines, the spirit drinker is not well catered for.

Where print advertising does work, however, is in promoting events such as open days and distillery tours, but don't try to do it on the cheap. A prominent position repays the higher price, although if you're a regular advertiser you'll get a pretty generous discount. And do change the copy frequently: the same ad used over and over again rapidly becomes completely invisible. Impact is everything in advertising, and it takes effort and expense to make sure your advertising maintains its impact.

Another, perhaps peripheral, area where print advertising has an impact is in promoting your shop/visitor centre, especially if you're in a tourist area. Leaflets in every hotel bedroom, b&b, pub and restaurant in town are guaranteed to bring in a certain amount of custom, especially when it's raining. Be sure to have plenty of miniatures, engraved glassware, tee-shirts and other less expensive impulse purchases in stock, and hopefully a few of the people attracted in this way will want to spend £30 and upwards on a bottle of whisky or gin. Make sure you also produce, a 37.5cl or 50cl option as this is a very useful addition to the portfolio.

## Merchandise

Actually the sort of merchandise just mentioned is in itself an effective form of advertising, with the advantage that all those branded polo-shirts, tee-shirts, shot-glasses and so on pay for themselves, even if you sell them more or less at cost. A branded shirt will be seen by thousands of people over the course of its natural life; a few dozen will be seen by hundreds of thousands. And they won't cost you a penny unless you're giving them away as promotional items – and even if you are, you're still getting a very, very good return on your investment in terms of public visibility. A good assortment of merchandise including a range of different bottle-sizes from miniature upwards is also a handy cache of tax-deductible raffle and tombola prizes for worthy local causes; and a reputation as a willing source of raffle and tombola prizes is, not to be too cynical about it, only another form of marketing.

## Awards and exhibitions

Some people question the value of awards – but only if they've never won one. But old jokes aside, the impact on consumer awareness of a cupboard full of silverware is dubious. The majority of awards are handed out by the trade to the trade, and the only consumers who ever get to hear about them are those who are interested enough to subscribe to specialist periodicals or through Twitter, Instagram and Facebook. Even as adornments to your bottle label, your point of sale material and your letterhead, the value of a bronze medal from this or that competition is somewhat limited by the fact that most shoppers know nothing and care less about the Grand Salon des Vins et Spiritueux de Grenouille-sur-Mer, or wherever you picked up your gong from. Not that a medal does any harm, of course, but how much good it does is... well, that's hard to measure, especially against entry fees that hover a bit north or south of £200 per sample (£130 + carriage for the UK-based International Wine & Spirits Competition; $300-400 for the New York International Spirits Competition).

Still, there's a value in entering as many competitions as you can afford, quite aside from your chances of winning a prize (which statistically are pretty good – 1,008 of the 1,474 entries in the last San Francisco World Spirits Competition came away with a gong), and that's exposure not to the public but to the trade. Buyers are always attracted to awards schemes (in fact the New York competition is judged entirely by trade buyers and bar owners) and it's not necessarily the medal-winners that catch their eye. And if you can make it to the presentation ceremony – which is inevitably an evening of boozy bonhomie – you have a very good chance indeed of meeting a person or people you can do good business with. Networking opportunities are rare in an industry that is geographically speaking fairly far-flung: they are not be sneezed at!

The best-known British awards schemes are probably the

International Wine & Spirits Competition (**www.iwsc.net**), judged in November, and the International Spirits Challenge (**www.internationalspiritschallenge.com**), judged in July. The World Drinks Awards (**www.worlddrinksawards.com**) is not a single competition but a series, one for each category, held throughout the year and organised by Norwich-based Paragraph Publishing, owner of *Whisky Magazine* and **www.thedrinksreport.com**.

American awards schemes are pretty international, too; and even if you can't afford to jet off to the awards dinner they offer you a good chance of catching the eye of importers and agents from all over the Americas and the Pacific Rim. Among them are the New York International Spirits Competition (**www.nyispiritscompetition.com**), the San Francisco World Spirits Competition (**www.sfspiritscomp. com**) and the Spirits International Prestige Awards (**www. sipawards.com**).

## Festivals and exhibitions

Just as important as awards in building a reputation among consumers are the various food festivals and exhibitions held around the country and, indeed, around the world. Whisky Live, for instance, is hosted in more than a dozen cities every year – 2017 saw events in London, Tokyo, Johannesburg, Los Angeles, Singapore, Taipei, Sydney and many other key cities – and attracts a horde of buyers as well as consumers. (For details visit **www.whiskylive.com.**) Also try out The Whisky Show in London (**www.whiskyshow.com**). Closer to home, the BBC Good Food Show is held at several centres throughout the year (**www.bbcgoodfoodshow.com**), while the much newer Craft Distilling Expo (**www.distill-ingexpo.com**), organised by the American Distillers' Institute and held at the old Truman brewery in the East End of London, is only in its fifth year but is proving a huge hit with savvy consumers.

Jet-setting aside, so many local and regional food

festivals are now listed on sites such as **www.thefestival calendar.co.uk** that the big question for craft distillers is which to attend. Their value is undeniable, because although they might attract much smaller crowds than higher-profile events like the BBC Good Food Show, every single person through the turnstiles is an enthusiast and a potential purchaser and they also attract local independent retailers looking for new lines to stock. On the other hand they can be quite expensive to attend if, as well as your stall fee, you have to find accommodation and petrol. The only way to decide which are the most relevant to you is to go to as many of them as you can – as a customer in the first instance, and only then as an exhibitor.

# Third-party retail

The traditional route to market is via third-party retailers – in the on-trade, dining pubs, restaurants and upscale hotel bars; in the off-trade specialist wine merchants, well-heeled farm shops and country house gift shops. The vast bulk of the mainstream retail trade, both on and off, is enormously hard to crack, though, because of the concentration of ownership in the hands of national pub companies, restaurant chains, and especially "multiple grocers" or, in the vernacular, supermarkets. Their corporate supply requirements and conditions – imposed for perfectly good reasons, perhaps – are effectively a barrier for most small artisanal producers. In Chapter Three: Getting Started we looked at finding local independent outlets as part of your market research; now is a good time to put your research to practical use.

## Local profile

Some spirits – especially whisky – are intensely local products. You can only get Bruichladdich from Bruichladdich, and its unique terroir – its water, its peat, the shape and size of its stills – is quite unlike any other distillery's. But spirits are also global products, traded all over the world regardless of their place of origin. The high value of the product means that, in comparison to beer, volume sales are low and the market is necessarily dispersed, so a craft distiller won't place the importance that most microbrewers would on a strong local sales round. Nevertheless, there are practical advantages in developing and maintaining a high local profile.

The first is that it's very good word-of-mouth. In the early days of microbrewing – and even today, if to a lesser extent – people were surprised and delighted to find that a small brewery was operating in their area: it gave them a greater sense of pride in their town or village, and they tended both to support its products and, equally important-ly, to talk about it. The same seems to be true of small distill-eries – "Did you know they'd started making gin at Brook-fields Farm...?" This sense of local pride might even lead to your brand becoming the house gin at the best restaurant or gastropub in the district, and repeat business is always the best.

The second is that it's easier and, in terms of time and petrol, cheaper to mount joint promotions with indepen-dent wine-merchants, restaurants and gastropubs (and not forgetting high-end farm shops and stately home gift shops) if they're only a few miles from the distillery rather than two or three counties away. Joint promotions such as tasting sessions are very good for business, not only for the sales you make on the night itself but also because of the fans you will make among local drinkers (and, quite possibly, the new business you might generate as a result – what if one of the satisfied tasters is secretary of the golf club?) and the working relationship you will develop with the host retail-ers. They will see that you are serious not just about winning accounts but about supporting those accounts, and they will

## Case Study – Warner Edwards
### www.warneredwards.com

Warner Edwards in the depths of rural Northamptonshire is a textbook example of how to build sales without expensive advertising, without supermarkets and without much in the way of facilities on site.

Founded in 2012 by agricultural college friends Tom Warner and Sion Edwards, the distillery is housed in an attractive early Victorian stone-built barn on the Warner family farm in Harrington, a small but pretty village (although it still has its pub, the Tollemache Arms) in the rolling arable land of Northamptonshire. But when Tom and Sion started out there was no immediate thought of exploiting the site itself: the farmyard is not huge, and the capital and human resources that would have been required to convert and operate any more of the buildings were required elsewhere. So the product was the attraction, not the site, and it had to be sold energetically.

The challenge was to spread the word on a shoestring. This being 2012, the arrival of a new gin distillery caused a certain amount of social media buzz and local media coverage, so the Warner Edwards name gained a foundation of awareness even before the partners hit the road. But hit the road they did, with an approach they describe as "scattergun" – trying every channel and building on what worked. The internet chatter and the trickle of visitors on after-hours tours generated a small income stream, but it was the ceaseless round of food festivals that got the company noticed.

Food festivals are not a panacea. You have to pay for your stall, for your petrol and for overnight accommodation; and driving to the venue, setting up, taking down and driving home again stretch a weekend event into four days. The costs are offset by bottle-sales and you might even turn a profit; but the real pay-off is meeting consumers and, more crucially, trade. Independent wine-merchants, delicatessen owners, farm shop proprietors – they're all sniffing round seeing which stalls are creating the most interest and looking for promising lines. You might not spot them, but if your stall is busy they'll spot you. And plenty of them spotted Warner Edwards.

The distillery's first full year was therefore a busy but successful one, with 14,000 bottles sold and a formidable list of stockists built up including two branches of Majestic Wine and all seven branches of Cambridge Wine Merchants. A silver medal at the San Francisco World Spirits Competition was more than just a vindication of quality, it was an introduction to the wider world. At a trade show in Belgium, Tom and Sion met an agent who now represents them in Benelux. By the end of the year they had the confidence to take on business development manager Harriet Roe.

"Our second year was just as busy as the first," she says. "By the end of 2014 we'd attended 60 shows and built up our base of independent retailers to more than 130. Our rhubarb gin was Gin of the Month at Fortnum & Mason, and to cap it all we were one of only nine gins to win double gold at San Francisco."

Success breeds success, and as the Warner Edwards name became better-known Harriet found herself dealing with unsolicited approaches from supermarkets including Booths, M&S, and Waitrose; from wholesalers, who have taken the brand into the on-trade including trendy London pub chain Drake & Morgan; and from America, both North and South. But success also demands hard graft, and Warner Edwards is grafting harder than ever. Exporting, for instance, can be both time-consuming and frustrating. "We once had an approach from Switzerland," says Harriet. "But Switzerland isn't in the EU, and can be even harder to deal with than the US – we had our first consignment turned back at the border twice!"

The growing network of UK retail customers demands servicing, too: wholesale customers will order whole pallets, but the few cases that go to each independent wine merchant have to go by courier, and independent retailers demand a lot of personal attention.

"We believe in supporting retail customers with as much activity as we can: they work hard for us and it's only right that we work hard for them," says Harriet. That means, mostly, after-hours tasting sessions for the shop's best regulars. Not so difficult when the account is a few miles down the road; tougher when it's in Penrith 196 miles away!

Since those early days Warner Edwards has had a chance to take another look at exploiting its site. The former tack room is now a bar and shop (called The Tack Room) and Tom's mother's garden has been planted up with almost all the botanicals the distillery needs (and is called The Botanical Garden). It's been a great success, not just hosting many local events but luring visitors from far and wide (and always recommending the Tollemache Arms and a local B&B in its publicity material, a sound step that endears the company to its neighbours and assures visitors that they're not venturing into a desert).

But it's the brands that matter most. The standard brand itself has won both praise and awards, but it was the Rhubarb Gin that proved to be a masterstroke in attracting attention. There's a sloe gin, of course, and an elderflower gin; the latest addition is more unusual – Melissa is named for the Melissa officinalis or lemon balm that comes from the Botanical Garden. Best drunk as a G&T that needs ice... but no slice!

appreciate it. After all, they will probably never even have met the regional sales manager of the Edrington Group or Pernod-Ricard; still less will they have had the boss of the company in person coming to the premises to entertain their patrons for a couple of hours!

## Making friends and influencing people

And finally, a strong local presence means you can build not just working relationships with high-end retailers of all stripes but personal relationships too. If you've managed to land two or three absolutely top-notch accounts by impressing them with the quality of your product, the joint promotions you want to organise, and the point of sale material that supports your brand, make the regular deliveries yourself. And when you do drop off the two or three cases they've ordered, make a point of asking if the chef-patron (or whoever) is about the place, and chat them up. It won't be long before you're a fixture and possibly even a minor celebrity on the local gastronomic circuit which, after all, is one of the big attractions of the job... and which makes good accounts much easier to hang on to. And it's the sort of friendship you can only strike up, in practical terms, with retailers within 20 or 30 miles of the distillery.

## Consignment trading

One objection you might encounter in selling to local independent retailers, though, is that many of them aren't particularly well-capitalised and feel that the wholesale price of your brand is simply too rich for their blood. In that case, if you think the account has potential, you fall back on consignment trading, which is like giving credit but not quite. You leave a case or two with them and come back a month or two later, when they pay you for what they've sold and you either take the unsold stock away with you or, if the retailer is pleased with throughput, you leave another case or two.

This sort of account is particularly worth supporting with promotional events, point of sale material and impulse packs such as 50cl bottles, half bottles and miniatures, because if the retailer feels that you're working hard on their behalf they're more likely to become regular accounts and to convert, after a trial period, from consignment to regular trading.

Consignment trading – provided your cash flow from other sources is strong enough – is also a good way of collaborating with other businesses like yours. Vineyards or cidermills with their own visitor centres, or local farm shops or specialist beer shops, might be looking for new and different lines to enhance their appeal to consumers but hesitant about tying up capital in premium spirits. Placing your product with them on a consignment basis – and promoting it! – makes you almost their partner and, especially if they like you, are start-ups, puts you in a strong position in the future.

## National accounts

Not all your third-party retailing need be local, mind. There are national retailers, or retailers a long way from your home base, who are well worth tackling. The sheer cachet of having your brand stocked by one of The Bunch – that elite group of independents comprising Adnams, Berry Brothers & Rudd, Corney & Barrow, Lea & Sandeman, Tanners of Shrewsbury and Yapp Brothers – will probably be matched by the volume of sales they can achieve on your behalf.

Majestic Wine (**www.majestic.co.uk**) and Oddbins (**www.oddbins.com**) also carry reasonably adventurous ranges of premium spirits although their main focus is, of course, wine. And why shouldn't you approach the buyers at magisterially intimidating emporia like Harrods and Fortnum & Mason? Your product is magnificent, and nowhere is too good for you.

## Internet trading

Pleasant and rewarding as personal friendships with local wine merchants and restaurateurs undoubtedly are, it is internet trading that will probably make or break you. Indirectly, in fact, most of your sales will quite probably be online either, as mentioned, via large internet traders such as Beers of Europe (whose spirits catalogue is absolutely astonishing), Master of Malt and Flaviar; via the websites of your retail stockists; or via your own website. And you will want to make as many sales as you possibly can through your own website, simply because they are more than twice as profitable: not only do you get to keep all the gross profit, but the channel carries almost no overhead. Warner Edwards, for instance, sells less than 10 per cent of its various gins on its own website but simple mathematics tells us that these sales account for 20 per cent or more of its GP.

How much effort you decide to devote to marketing via social media such as Facebook, Twitter, Instagram and blogging depends on how relevant you think these platforms are to your target demographic audience and how proficient you are at operating them, but if you do strive to create a high profile on social media make sure you are directing customers towards your own website to do their purchasing.

The potential rewards are huge, especially among the younger demographics; but be warned: although social media are free of charge they can become extremely time-consuming, and rely for their effectiveness on your ability to make the best use of them. If your gin or vodka have a following among the younger, hipper crowd and a sizeable proportion of your stockists are chic metropolitan cocktail bars, you might very well feel that social media is essential. But if you yourself have any doubts about your control over the technology or your ability to speak the right language, outsource. It'll cost, but this is one area where it's all too easy to get things wrong and expose yourself and your brand to ridicule.

## Licensed to trade online

However enthusiastically or otherwise you plunge into the world of social media, one thing you will need before you start trading is a premises licence; and even though your internet customers will never set foot inside your distillery the local council's requirements will be exactly the same as if you were proposing to run a pub or a nightclub (although they might very well be applied rather less rigorously). And, unlike getting a personal licence, this is no small matter.

We shall go more deeply into the ins and outs of getting your premises licence below; suffice it to say for now that it will take at least two months between your application and the grant of your licence; that you will have to supply detailed drawings of your premises to accompany the application; and that you will have to display the application outside your premises for 28 days to give the neighbours a chance to object. The requisite form will be on your local council's website, and a fee will be charged.

## Couriers

Licensing may have become more complicated since the 2003 Act came in, but one thing that has become much easier is finding a courier who will not only deliver fragile items such as bottles of gin but even specialises in them, giving advice on packaging and offering insurance.

In the early days of internet trading, it was Hobson's choice – you took what you were offered, and many pioneers changed couriers several times before finding someone reliable. These days the choice is much wider: even Royal Mail Parcelforce will ship glass, which once upon a time it refused to do. Unlike some, it doesn't provide any insurance, so you will have to take out a policy of your own, but its one great advantage over the competition is that if a customer misses a delivery it won't have to be rearranged: the parcel will simply be left safely at the nearest Post Office or sorting office for the customer to collect at their leisure.

# Premises licence

As noted above, you will need a premises licence before you begin internet trading, but one way of expanding your business is to develop a retail operation at the distillery, which will also, of course, require a premises licence.

It's not everyone's cup of tea – if you are the intense, near-obsessive type you might prefer your workspace to be a Trappist haven of concentration, and it may very well be that you're not the cheery, outgoing sort who relishes or is especially good at the flirtation that inevitably goes with front-of-house work. Nevertheless, there are advantages to making your distillery a tourism hub, depending on where in the country you settle and what sort of premises you occupy. If there weren't, then more than half of Scotland's 170 (and counting) malt distilleries wouldn't have visitor facilities at all levels from pre-booked tours up through shops, cafes, smart restaurants and museum-style exhibitions all the way to integral b&bs, often in the cottages where distillery workers once lived. But there are disadvantages too, so let's deal with them first.

## Entertaining the customers

The biggest is that if you decide to throw open your doors to the public, you have to do it properly. People won't part with their pence, let alone give all their friends a glowing report when they get home, unless they've had an experience that matched their expectations. And let's face it, distilling is an industrial process that, unless you gussy it up something rotten, isn't exactly Formula 1. Once the visitor has taken in the visual appeal of the gleaming copper and the spirit bubbling away inside it... well, there's not all that much actually going on. That leaves you having to create something to grab and keep their interest – a museum, or a multimedia presentation of some description, or both, all of which will involve you in time, effort and expense you can't necessarily justify.

The first risk, then, in adapting your business to the demands of tourism is loss of focus: of becoming a tourist attraction first and a manufacturer second. This is not necessarily a bad strategy, depending on your location and circumstances, but is not something you want to slip into by accident.

## Making it pay

And that neatly takes us to the second great danger of allow-ing the public untrammelled access to your site: the costs involved can easily run away with you. One or two Scotch whisky distilleries with once-popular visitor centres have withdrawn from the tourism market altogether because outlay on the provision of facilities such as car parking, customer toilets and access for people with disabilities, and overheads such as maintenance, utilities and staff wages, and the constant need to reinvest to keep the place looking fresh were shoving the cart inexorably in front of the horse.

That notwithstanding, a modest shop – perhaps with a coffee machine and a WC – will probably turn out to be a great asset, if only as a marshalling and sampling area for visitors on distillery tours. Unless, that is, your distillery really is on an industrial estate surrounded by urban waste-land where no-one would venture except on business – and even then, you might choose to run a shop, perhaps as a joint venture with other local food and drink producers, in an attractive and upmarket primary location nearby.

But even if your shop is so modest as to be not much

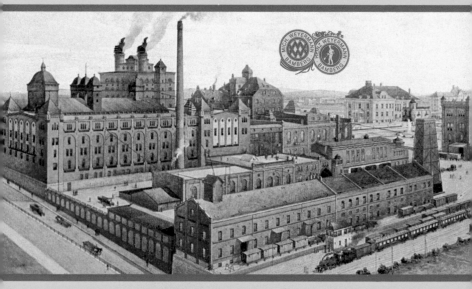

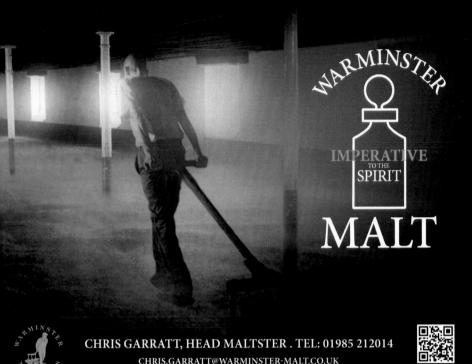

more than a spruced-up reception area, you will still need your premises licence.

## Applying for a premises licence

After your initial planning application and your application for a distiller's licence, your premises licence application is likely to be one of the biggest challenges you'll ever be faced with.

One difference between the 2003 Licensing Act and the 1964 Act that went before it is that the law today requires licensees to be much more public-spirited than they used to be. Not only must they understand and swear to uphold public policy on alcohol-related disorder, protection of minors and so on; they also have to consult the police and fire services as well as the local community, who will all have a say on the conditions the local council decides to impose.

In one sense this is a headache for licensees. On the one hand, getting a new licence or having an existing one varied is far more costly and time-consuming than it used to be. On the other hand, though, it's also far more permanent in that you only have to jump through the hoops once, because the Act also abolished the requirement to renew your licence at the annual Brewster Sessions. So once you've got it, you're on a much more secure footing than you used to be. Provided you respect the terms of your licence, it's hard for the police or neighbours to get it revoked or even reviewed. You've filed your flight plan, as it were, in exhaustive detail and everyone concerned has had a chance to suggest alterations and restrictions. Everything has been openly negotiated and agreed, and as long as you stick to the operating schedule that the council has approved, nobody (in theory, at least) has anything to complain about.

## Public consultation

As mentioned earlier, the new-look licensing procedure is principally about consultation and ensuring that you understand your responsibilities. There's a fearsome-looking 16-page form to fill in, but if you download it from your local council's website and give it a thorough read you'll see that much of it isn't relevant to you. That's one of the (admittedly slight, in this case) drawbacks to the new one-stop licensing procedure: a single form has to cover every licensable activity including showing films, putting on plays, promoting boxing matches and so on, which makes it a pretty bulky document. (By the way, and although the form doesn't say so, the section covering "performance of dance" specifically excludes folk dancers).

But most of it isn't concerned with liquor licensing at all and need not concern you, and the trickier sections, such as those to do with carrying out the council's licensing objectives, will have been covered in the training course you completed when you got your personal licence. The form, then, is fairly simple – you shouldn't need a solicitor to help you fill it out, and it should only take you a day or at most two.

But the form is only the last part of the application process. You will also need to advertise your application in the manner prescribed by the licensing authority (which is not a new requirement); you will need to submit an accurate and intelligible plan of the premises, although hiring a proper draughtsman to do it probably won't be necessary; and you will need to submit copies to the "responsible authorities" (fire, police and so on) as stipulated by the licensing authority. Just as important as correctly observing the formalities is to consult as widely as possible in advance, both with neighbours (and the term "interested parties" includes schools and businesses as well as residents) and with the "responsible authorities" and the council's licensing officers. As with your planning application, if you do your homework thoroughly the application you finally submit should be bomb-proof.

## Work with the council, not against it

The key to dealing with council licensing officers, as with HMRC and planning officers, is to be calm, rational, and friendly and not regard them as jobsworths to be either bamboozled or placated or both. If treated with respect they can be – and indeed most of them want to be – extremely helpful, and can give you the advice that makes sure your application succeeds.

They can suggest ways in which the four licensing policy objectives can be met, many of which you may not have thought of. They will give you many invaluable tips, such as how to present the general description of the premises (section 3 of the application form) and the more detailed operating schedule as flexibly as possible, so you don't have to keep varying your licence whenever you want to try something new.

They will have issues of their own to raise, too: you might, for instance, be in or near an area where public drinking is prohibited, and they may ask what steps you propose to deter customers from buying takeaways to drink in the street. (The best answer to this is to stress that your shop, if you have one, won't be selling cheap cans of lager or cider but extremely expensive bottles of hand-crafted spirits – although once you've made this commitment you will be bound by it.)

## Planning for promotional events

They will also want to know what provisions you have in mind regarding open days and other large public events, specifically for parking, toilets, noise abatement, control of numbers and public disorder contingency planning.

Going into this kind of detail at this embryonic stage might be a bit over the top, but it's as well to have considered such matters as site layout, advance publicity and limiting numbers even at this early stage. Because the value of possessing a site that's licensed to do pretty much anything is that as your business evolves you can do – well, pretty much anything.

# Export sales

Export sales are likely to become more and more important as the craft distilling movement gathers pace and the domestic market becomes more and more crowded. Fortunately, and thanks to the tradition of quality gained over generations of fine whisky and gin distilling, British-made spirits have a huge reputation in the key overseas markets – so much so that you may well find foreign buyers and enthusiasts approaching you before you've even considered how to approach them. Reaching foreign buyers via awards schemes and trade exhibitions, as above, is also an important step towards supplying this demand.

Dealing with the risks and complications of exporting to foreign jurisdictions, however, is a formidable barrier and the best thing you can do is turn first to your bank and then to the Government for sound advice and practical help.

## Safety first

Your bank will encourage you, as banks are wont to do, to sit down before plunging in and have a good think not just about the potential but about the potential risk. The first and most obvious consideration your adviser at the bank will bring up with you is production volume: if your gin is a runaway hit in Spain, can you supply the demand? Are you in a financial position to expand production at short notice if necessary?

## City of London Distillery
### www.cityoflondondistillery.com

So where are all the boutique distillery bars? By this stage in the microbrewing revolution, brewpubs were commonplace: any old outhouse (even an outside loo) would comfortably accommodate a five-barrel plant, and with most of the on-trade still denied to microbrewers by the tie, having a pub of your own as your primary sales channel, with wholesaling as the icing on the cake, made perfect sense. Surely, therefore, a distillery bar is equally desirable. Gin has taken centre stage in upmarket bars in the smarter quarters of cities across the country. Isn't a cocktail lounge with the still in situ the logical next step?

There must be something holding back the emergence in large numbers of what ought to be the Next Big Thing – so what can it be?

Well, it's the maths. A well-engineered gin still is at least twice as expensive as a good-quality five-barrel brewery: more than £50,000 compared to maybe £25,000. It needs plenty of ancillaries, too: for instance, a decent bottling plant complete with bottles and fancy labels, all of which, unlike casks and pump-clips, are thrown away after a single use.

Then there's location. Ale lovers will travel for miles to a brewpub with a good reputation; but for the gin generation location – usually somewhere where the rents have already gone through the roof and are reaching for the stars – is critically important. They don't come to you: you have to be where they are. And while the standard of decor isn't going to make or break a brewpub – the scruffier the better, for some aficionados – a gin-joint has to be chic, and even shabby chic doesn't come cheap.

All this investment has to be recouped from the takings of what is, after all, only a bar. It works for brewpubs, many of which are only marginally involved in wholesaling, but it would have to be a pretty special bar that could repay the entire investment required to set up a distillery. But that's what the first of the trail-blazers, the City of London Distillery in Bride Lane off Fleet Street, which opened in November 2012, set out to do.

CoLD is as well-located as it could possibly be. The stylish bar is a popular lunchtime and early evening venue in exactly the right part of town, and is also a unique corporate hire. And then there are the various distillery tours ranging from £10 for a simple look round to £125 for the Gin Lab Experience, with a large number of TripAdvisor reviews, 80 per cent of them "excellent". It's not that CoLD owner Jonathan Clark doesn't want people to buy his gin at £32.50 a pop from his online shop, and indeed it is available in some branches of Waitrose. But the primary focus of the business is the site itself.

"I was going to put a microbrewery on the site, but I saw this idea in the States and really thought it was more original and interesting," says Clark. He originally planned a small chain of distillery bars in other big cities but has now shelved the idea. "It's a hard business. It would be easy to invest a lot of money and lose it."

Location, he says, would be the key; and a site's suitability would have to be judged not just by its prominence but more by the established local custom. A bar intended for a sophisticated and affluent clientele would work in a district of restaurants, theatres and good hotels, but would be an instant failure in a district favoured by binge-drinking clubbers.

## Bow Wharf Bar
### www.eastlondonliquorcompany.com/bowwharf.html

London's second distillery bar is just as well-located as CoLD but in a different way. The Bow Wharf Bar, opened in late 2014, occupies a canalside Victorian factory building in gentrified Hackney where the gleaming Holstein stills are on display behind glass screens, but the bar was only phase one in the development of the East London Liquor Company and its takings were never intended to be the main income stream. The bar is nothing like big enough, and its clientele is nothing like rich enough to account for a significant proportion of the distillery's output. This is a distillery with a bar rather than a bar with a distillery; but the bar generated critical cash-flow while the East London Liquor Company's other main activities – importing, maturing and bottling single-estate rums from Guyana and malt whiskies from California, and distilling its own whisky – gathered momentum.

"Within eight weeks of opening we'd sold 6–7,000 bottles of gin and vodka, and half of our sales were over the bar," says owner Alex Wolpert, but as anticipated the bar's share of sales has diminished as other channels have developed.

So Britain's first distillery bars are not only very different from brewpubs: they're also very different from each other. But will they come to play as important part in the future of craft distilling as brewpubs have done in microbrewing?

Wolpert is a little more confident than Clark that we will see more distillery bars in future, but agrees that the scale of the investment means it's not to be undertaken lightly.

"The decision to make that kind of investment will always have to be very site-specific," he says. "And there will generally have to be a diverse marketing strategy that doesn't depend entirely on the bar – after all, it's no good installing £350,000-worth of distilling equipment if all you're going to do is sell beer!"

This is a key question, because the last thing you want to do is to create expectations and immediately disappoint them: once you get a reputation for unreliability among distributors and stockists it's very hard to get rid of – there will be plenty of competitors eager to move in on the accounts you have lost, and luring those disgruntled clients back will be harder than it was to win them in the first place.

You might consider withdrawing completely from a market where you haven't done well in order to supply one where you are succeeding, but then when you come to have a second go at the first market you'll find it harder to win the confidence of the liquor trade there. Best not to go crazy and try to invade the whole of Europe or Latin America all at once: have a plan that will allow you to increase production at short notice – enough money and HMRC's permission to install a second set of stills, say – and then take it one country at a time.

## Interjurisdictional trading agreements

Second, your bank will ask you what kind of operating model you propose. If you have a dispute with a trading partner, for example, which jurisdiction will it be decided in, yours or theirs? Get this written unambiguously into any agreement you make.

And what sort of trading partnership will suit you best? Most first-time exporters will depend heavily on an established agent or representative, but it has to be the right agent – one who understands not only your product but also the size and ambitions of your operation – and especially, one who genuinely wants to get behind your product rather than merely add it to an ever-growing portfolio of neglected minority brands.

Further down the line you might consider a joint venture with an importer who will concentrate exclusively on your brands rather than a more general portfolio; further still (and this is probably quite some way away!), you might set up your own wholly-owned subsidiaries in export markets.

But again, it's baby steps at first, and you have to be prepared (i.e., you have to have money in the bank) for setbacks such as an agent who turns out not to be much of a salesman or, worse still, one who sells thousands and thousands of pounds' worth of your product and then disappears with your money.

There is every chance, if you are serious about exporting, that one day you might find yourself taking legal action in a completely unfamiliar jurisdiction where you don't even speak the language. Every jurisdiction has different laws regarded intellectual property, and you have to be protected in each jurisdiction you trade with. Your bank will advise you on all aspects of how to prepare against such a horrible but far from unheard of emergency, from writing cast-iron agreements to suing; if it doesn't, change banks.

## Exchange rates

While the relationship between sterling, the euro, and the dollar is usually (relatively) stable, and you should be able to balance out the minor (again, relatively!) fluctuations over time, a currency collapse or an outbreak of hyperinflation in a more volatile market can catch you out catastrophically. With the UK now leaving the EU, the exchange rate of euro to UK Sterling will have to be monitored even more closely. That million-escudo deal looked fine and dandy when a million escudos was worth £50,000; but if it's lost 90 per cent of its value by the time your trading partner actually pays you, you may find yourself in doo-doo of irrecoverable depth. Again, your bank should be able to forearm you against all but the worst eventuality in this regard.

The government is more than usually obliging when it comes to preparing to tackle the export trade, and there are two government websites in particular that will help to get you started: **www.greatbusiness.gov.uk/ukti** will put you in touch with UK Trade & Investment and its one-to-one expert advice service, while **www.gov.uk/starting-to-export** explains and helps you apply for an array of grants, loans and insurance schemes. There are small grants for travel to overseas trade fairs, research grants, bridging finance, loan support for when your bank proves a bit sticky and a range of other loans for specific purposes. There's also a link to Passport to Export which explains how Export Credit Guarantees will pay you if one of your overseas customers for some reason doesn't.

Finally, and in some ways most useful of all, **www.opentoexport.com** is run jointly by UKTI and the British Chambers of Commerce and as well as carrying scores of useful articles and other documents enables you to post questions of your own and, surprisingly often, find yourself in direct personal contact with foreign importers who can not only answer any jurisdictional queries you might have but are also quite likely to become your trading partners – a government-sponsored dating service for lonely-heart exporters, in fact.

### The bonded warehouse and Notice 197

Given HMRC's rigorous assiduity in protecting government revenues, the movement of excise goods in duty suspension in and around (and outside) the EU is regulated in minute detail by Notice 197: Receipt Into and Removal From an Excise Warehouse of Excise Goods. This will be become a lot more compliated once Brexit has been negotiated. Those sections dealing with movements within the UK are summarised in Appendix III, but if you happily find yourself with export orders to fill, you will want to familiarise yourself with the rest of the Notice. Give yourself plenty of time – it's a big read!

08

# Appendices

# Appendix I HMRC Notice 36

### Notice 39: Spirits production in the United Kingdom

It is your responsibility to exercise control over all aspects of your spirit production including the physical security of your premises, plant, vessels etc; the security of spirits produced; accounting for the spirits produced; rendering returns on time; the examination of losses and identifying their cause; the investigation of any irregularity at your premises; and the implementation and monitoring of reasonable and effective measures to prevent any loss of dutiable spirits. You should make sure your production records take these aspects into account. You may be penalised if you fail to comply with the law.

### Approvals and licences

Before you start to produce spirits you must obtain a distiller's licence and apply for approval of the plant and process you intend to use. To apply for a licence complete an application form and send it to:

HM Revenue & Customs
National Registration Unit
Portcullis House
21 India St
Glasgow, G2 4PZ.
Tel 0141 555 3489/3586
Fax 0141 555 3506

You should make the application in the name of the person manufacturing the spirits. If you, as manufacturer, are not also the owner of the premises you may obtain a licence in joint names. If you intend to produce spirits at more than one set of premises you must get a licence for each.

The production of spirits by a person who is not licensed is an offence for which there is a penalty. For information on penalties, go to **http://www.hmrc.gov.uk/about/new-penalties/faqs.htm**.

HMRC may refuse to issue a licence or revoke an existing licence where the largest still to be used has a capacity below 18 hectolitres, or when you cease to manufacture spirits.

To apply for approval of plant and process write to the National Registration Unit providing the following details:

- the location of the proposed distillery
- a full description of the manufacturing process
- the number and description of the vessels used in the manufacturing process and use of all plant, and
- a plan of the premises.

It is advisable not to acquire land or premises or begin any building operations until HMRC approves your plans. Approval may include conditions which will be reviewed from time to time and may be added to or varied. Significant changes to plant (eg the addition or removal of production vessels) must be notified in writing to the National Registration Unit.

As a producer of spirits (distiller) your premises will be a tax warehouse. Under EU legislation, this is a place where exciseable goods can be produced, processed, held, received and dispatched under duty-suspension arrangements. This does not permit you to receive or store duty unpaid alcohol at your distillery. Spirits may only be received and stored in an excise or distiller's warehouse.

## Records and Accounts

The following requirements have the force of law under regulation 6 of the Revenue Traders (Account & Records) Regulations 1992.

You must keep records of all your spirit production. This includes information on processes and operations such as fermentations; distillations, including the start and finish of each distillation period and any process or stage of the process in the manufacture of spirits; and deliveries to the warehouse.

Your normal business records should be enough, but HMRC may ask you to modify them if needed. They do not have to be kept in any particular format, but they must be accurate and up-to-date, completed in ink or other permanently legible material, readily accessible to HMRC and kept for at least six years from the date of the last entry. You must not remove any pages from your records, or obliterate any entry without HMRC's prior agreement. You can keep computerised records, but you must inform HMRC in advance. Your system must be capable of producing readable print-outs whenever requested. HMRC will advise you if you need to make any changes to your system.

You must also keep all records and documents relating to stock; handling; purchases; sales; imports and exports. HMRC may also wish to look at profit and loss and trading statements; management accounts and reports; balance sheets; internal and external auditor's reports and any other business record. Any incidents which affect operations, for example a breakdown of plant, must also be recorded accurately.

## Security and construction of premises and plant

You are responsible for the security of the spirit until the duty is paid. HMRC will check your security systems, and you must pay duty on any losses you cannot explain. HMRC recommends the following security measures and checks.

Distillery: perimeter and building security which deters casual entry and shows signs of forced entry; regular security reviews.

Stillroom and warehouse: restricted access and regular checks of vessels and plant; frequent management checks to ensure any lapses in security are put right.

Vessels and plant: measures to ensure that all vessel openings are locked or sealed and that signs of tampering or pilferage do not go unnoticed; technology that controls access to all areas and vessels on the site.

HMRC also expects all plant to be accessible, readily identifiable and with the exception of working stills, capable of being opened as required for inspection; and that all wash backs, feints receivers and spirit receivers should be gauged and calibrated, with calibration tables readily available.

## Manufacturing operations

Distillation periods are accounting periods during which you must carry out all your manufacturing of spirits. A period is usually between a week and a month. If you need a longer period you should contact the Excise Helpline, by calling 0300 200 3700. You must specify the start and finish dates of each period in your records. If you manufacture more than one class of spirits (see below) you must specify separate periods for each class of spirit. These periods may run simultaneously. Every distillation period should be clearly identifiable in your business records.

You must complete form W21 Quarterly Distillery Return – Declaration of Materials Used and Spirits Produced, at the end of March, June, September, and December. You will need to complete a separate return for each class of spirits you produce. Each distillery has a unique five-digit identifying number. If you manufacture more than one class of spirits you will be allocated a unique number for each class. You may be liable to a penalty if your return is inaccurate and, as a result, you do not pay enough duty or if you do not notify HMRC that a duty assessment is too low. If you know you have made a mistake on your return, you must notify them as soon as possible: they may be able to reduce the penalty. If you deliberately make a false duty return, you may face prosecution for the offence and incur a heavy penalty.

When you manufacture spirits you may use only the processes for which you have received approval, and comply with any conditions HMRC has specified. If you wish to change an existing process or use a new process contact the Excise Helpline, by calling 0300 200 3700.

Duty-unpaid samples of wort, wash, feints and spirits may be taken for the purposes of quality control, strength testing, scientific research, reference, and other production-related analysis. However, you must note the samples taken in your business records, keep the quantity to the minimum necessary, label the samples as 'duty-unpaid sample – not for sale,' destroy samples no longer required and keep records of their use and disposal.

## Measuring wort, wash and gravity

You must measure the quantity and gravity of wort and wash collected using recognised industry methods and equipment, in accordance with the manufacturer's protocol, and keep accurate records.

Instruments for measuring alcoholic strength, including automatic densimeters, must comply with regulation 18 of the Spirits Regulations 1991 (as amended). The density must be directly measured as density in air, not density in vacuum converted to density in air, and the temperature of the liquid must be 20°C – the measurement cannot be taken at a different temperature and converted to the equivalent density at 20°C. All of the approved densimeters have been five decimal place machines, and when used according to the instructions have proved to be accurate and precise enough for HMRC. Some machines can convert the density of a liquid to the alcoholic strength from an internal look-up table. Such machines must use the Official HMRC

Laboratory Alcohol Tables to convert the density in air value to an alcoholic strength.

## Low wines, feints and spirits

You may remove any fusel oil which has separated from the feints in the feints receiver, or collected in oil traps, but you must measure the quantity and strength of the fusel oil before you dispose of it and record the details in your records. Duty is not charged on fusel oil which is below 8.7 per cent ABV, but no spirits or feints should be mixed with the oil. If it contains more than 8.7 per cent alcohol by volume, it must be 'washed' so that the ABV is reduced to 8.7 per cent or below before it is removed from the distillery. If the strength of any fusel oil is greater than 8.7 per cent, the whole product is liable to duty at the spirits rate.

Normally you will carry feints forward from one manufacturing period to another. If you have feints which you no longer wish to use in the manufacture of spirits, these should be isolated and an account taken of them. They should then be warehoused or destroyed. Your records must show what you have done with the feints. If you destroy or dispose of feints you will need to alter your Whisky Export Refund Scheme claim. You may re-distil low wines and feints at any time. You should ensure that the details of operations to re-distil low wines, feints and spirits are recorded in your business records.

## Accounting for and warehousing of spirits

You must keep a record of the spirits you have produced. The record must include the following details:

- the date and time
- the receiver or other vessel
- the dip or gauge reading
- the temperature and hydrometer readings, and
- the quantity of spirits, adjusted to a temperature of

20°C, with details of bulk volume, strength, and
*   litres of alcohol produced.

The spirits should be sent to an approved warehouse immediately after you have entered the details of the spirits account in your business records. If your spirit receiver is also approved as a warehouse vat, they will consider the spirits to be warehoused as soon as the account has been taken and declared in your records. You can find further information about distiller's warehouses in Notice 197 Excise Goods: Receipt into and Removal from an Excise Warehouse of Excise Goods.

## Duty

Excise duty is not normally payable until the spirits are taken out of warehouse (for examples of the excise duty calculation for spirits, see Notice 197), but you may be asked to pay duty on any losses that occur at your distillery or while transferring spirits to a warehouse, which are not due to natural wastage or for which you do not have a valid reason. Duty is normally based on the litres of alcohol contained in the spirits and feints less the litres of alcohol in feints brought forward from the previous period. This is known as the actual charge. The rate of duty on spirits is shown in Part 12, Volume 1, of the integrated Tariff of the United Kingdom which can be found either on **www.hmrc. gov.uk** or by phoning the Excise Helpline, 0300 200 3700.

If the amount of spirits produced is not what you expected you should investigate the reasons why this has happened. Your business records should show the steps you have taken to look into the matter and your findings. If, having completed your investigations, you have found no satisfactory explanation for the loss, then you should provide a written explanation of what has happened. HMRC may assess for duty on the loss.

# Appendix II: HMRC Notice 196

**Notice 196: Excise goods – authorisation of warehouse-keepers and approval of premises**

## Approvals, authorisations and registrations

Only persons who can demonstrate that they are fit and proper to carry out an excise business will be authorised or registered as excise warehousekeepers. Failure to apply for authorisation or approval at the correct time can attract a financial penalty.

HMRC will visit the authorised excise warehouse-keepers and approved premises of excise goods in duty-suspension to carry out checks on production, operations and warehousing. If you do not provide safe access, HMRC will restrict or withdraw your authorisation.

The warehousekeeper must display prominently the warning poster Notice 50 Duty-free warehouse warning at each entrance and exit to the site. Notice 50 explains that excise goods in the warehouse may be duty-suspended and that improperly removing them may incur severe penalties including imprisonment.

HMRC will normally arrange appointments to visit but may also make unannounced visits. You must permit HMRC officers access to any area of the warehouse during operating hours or at any time when activity is taking place at the warehouse.

## Applying for authorisation

To apply for authorised excise warehousekeeper status, complete Form EX61 Excise Warehousekeeper – Application for Registration, which is available from the HMRC website. If you are a partnership you must also complete form EXCISE 102.

The application form must be completed and signed by the sole proprietor, one of the partners if the business, or a director or the company secretary or an authorised signatory. Completed forms should be returned to the National Registration Unit (NRU).

You must apply at least 45 working days before the date on which you wish your authorisation to begin to allow HMRC time to carry out the necessary verification and pre-approval checks, which will include a visit. Your application will be vetted and is subject to background checks. Should these checks provide insufficient assurance that the business is suitable for authorisation, further information may be requested. Until this information is received, your application will be put on hold.

During the visit HMRC will examine all the business's activities and may enquire about its suppliers, customers, business plans, accounting systems, premises, financial viability and so on. Only when it is satisfied the business is a genuine enterprise which is commercially viable, with a genuine need for authorisation and that all key persons are fit and proper to carry on such a business will it process the application.

Reasons for refusing an application may include circumstances where:

- The legal entity (this includes the directors and key employees) has been involved in revenue non-compliance or fraud.
- The application is incomplete or inaccurate.
- You (the directors in the case of a limited company) have unspent convictions.
- There are proven links between the legal entity or key employees with other known non-compliant or fraudulent businesses.
- The business is not commercially viable.
- You have not been able to demonstrate the business is genuine.
- You have outstanding HMRC debts

- The legal entity has been involved in significant revenue non-compliance.
- You are unable to provide adequate financial security.
- You do not have a satisfactory accounting system.
- If HMRC is not satisfied with the information pro vided to us, it may refuse to authorise you. If you fail to provide the information requested, it will place your application on hold until it is received. It will notify you of the reason or reasons for refusal.

## Record keeping

Record-keeping requirements are laid down in Notice 206 Revenue traders records. All records must be permanent and legible and must show details of all excise goods received, stored in and removed from the warehouse. Your stock accounts must show:

- A full description of the goods (including age and date of first warehousing for spirits).
- The current location of goods in the warehouse.
- The duty status of the goods, and evidence of any duties paid.
- The name, address and, if appropriate, the VAT Registration Number of the owner, and, if applicable, the duty representative.
- Whether the goods have been subject to a supply in warehouse, and
- A means of identifying all goods to their stock number or vice versa.

If you wish to use computers for stock control and/or accounting purposes you should include this request in your application for approval, providing full details of the system you intend to adopt. The standard of records stored on your computer must be equivalent to that required if you were to use manual records.

When considering granting approval to use your specified software package HMRC requires:

- Right of access to your computer systems and to data and documentation including financial and management systems.
- The facility to download data for checks and audit work off-site.
- Any necessary assistance in carrying out audits of your systems.
- Adequate back-up and disaster recovery systems.
- A terminal for official use capable only of printing, reading files, and displaying information on the VDU.
- A unique password to allow officers access to files on a read-only basis.

## Stock marking and control

You must mark all excise goods so that you can identify them in your stock accounts. Excise goods must have clear and tamper-proof markings at all times from arrival at to removal from duty-suspension. You may use any system which meets this requirement (for example, bar coding), providing that you can establish an audit trail.

Your stock account must show:

- a commercial description of the product
- the quantity received in litres of alcohol
- the alcoholic strength of the product
- the quantity received in cases, casks and/or poly-drums
- a unique identifying reference number
- the date received
- the owner of the goods.

You should keep all excise goods in clearly identified locations so that you can readily trace them to the stock account.

You must note the appropriate stock account whenever you move excise goods to a new location in the warehouse. You must check the accuracy of your stock by undertaking a satisfactory inventory-checking system as agreed with HMRCand by complete stocktaking at reasonable intervals. You must take stock of all excise goods in the excise warehouse monthly in the case of bulk goods in vats or in storage tanks or annually in the case of all other excise goods. HMRC may ask you to produce all stocktaking records and working papers and carry out a stocktake if there is reasonable cause.

As authorised warehousekeeper, you are responsible for control of the goods in your approved sites. You must take all necessary steps to control and safeguard your stocks and investigate and examine critically all losses and deficiencies.

You must record all the losses and the results of your investigations into them, including any management decisions taken, take prompt remedial action, report losses or deficiencies to HMRC and note the loss in the stock account.

Failure to report notifiable losses immediately is a serious breach of your conditions of approval, and could lead to its revocation. HMRC will charge duty on losses and deficiencies unless you can show they are due to natural causes or accident. Your records must contain a clear audit trail to justify any adjustments of stock records following the discovery of any errors. If at any time you discover a discrepancy in your stock you must immediately contact the Excise and Customs Helpline on 0300 200 3700.

## General storage and distribution warehouses

To apply for General Storage and Distribution Warehouse ('bonded warehouse') approval, use form EX68. To gain approval you should have a minimum potential duty liability of £500,000 on the average monthly stockholding of duty-suspended goods, or a duty liability of at least £2,000,000 on an annual throughput.

## Trade facility warehouses

A trade facility warehouse is approved for a specific purpose that has to be completed within duty suspension; for example, a bottling operation. Approval will stipulate the period that duty-suspended goods may be stored on the premises before and after the approved activity takes place. Once the purpose of the trade facilitation has been completed, the goods must either be duty-paid, removed to a warehouse approved to store such goods or exported. Complete form EX69 to apply.

## Financial guarantees

An approved guarantor (for example, a financial institution) must undertake to pay HMRC in the event of a chargeable loss where the person liable fails to pay. Authorised warehousekeepers should contact the Financial Securities Centre (FSC) for further details about applying for a premises guarantee. Guarantees are the only form of security acceptable to HMRC. Only companies approved by HMRC may act as guarantors. Most banks and insurance companies have this approval. The cost of maintaining the guarantee is a commercial arrangement between you and the guarantor.

Your liability is not restricted to the size of the guarantee. HMRC can assess the liability for outstanding duty arising from any chargeable loss in the warehouse which may be significantly greater than the size of the guarantee.

For general storage and distribution warehouses HMRC will base the level of security on the potential duty due on average end-of-month stock calculated over a 12-month period, allowing for any seasonal variations. For trade facility warehouses it bases its calculation on the proposed or current throughput levels.

The minimum level of security for new general storage and distribution warehouses is £250,000.

HMRC will offer a reduction of the guarantee levels for

| Potential duy on month-end stock holding | Level of Security |
|---|---|
| <£100,000 | Nil |
| >£100,000 but <£400,000 | £100,000 |
| >£400,000 but <£1m | 25 per cent of potential duty |
| >£1m but <£25m | £250,000 |
| >£25m but <£100m | 1 per cent of potential dury |
| >£100m | £1m |

established traders if it has made no claim against the security and no significant irregularities have been identified.

Where the principal qualifies for a reduction in the level of security and the new security required would be less than £100,000, no security is required.

As an authorised warehousekeeper you must inform the FSC if your trading pattern changes, as it could result in an increased or reduced level of guarantee.

In the following circumstances its may allow reductions for premises security as follows:

## Approval to carry out operations in warehouse

The only allowable operations in distillers' warehouses are:
- bottling of spirits produced at the associated distillery
- reducing spirits with water
- filling casks or drums with spirits

- removing spirits in bulk by tanker or authorised pipeline
- drawing off spirits from unsound casks or pumping direct from casks to tanker
- emptying casks into vats for removal in bulk
- transferring spirits from cask to cask
- If you wish to carry out an operation that is not listed above or are in any doubt that your action is allowable, contact the Helpline on 0300 200 3700, giving full details of the proposed operation

| If the principal has | And HMRC has | The level of security is reduced |
|---|---|---|
| Provided security for the two previous consecutive years. | Made no claim against the security and no significant irregularities have been identified. | By 50 per cent |
| Provided security for the previous four consecutive years. | Made no claim against the security and no significant irregularities have been identified. | No guarantee is required. |

When carrying out any operation on duty-suspended goods, you must take accurate records immediately before and after each operation, keep an accurate record of any cleaning agent used, and advise HMRC about any gains and losses from any operation in the warehouse.

For each bottling operation you must:
- take account prior to bottling
- take and record bottle measurements of strength and liquid content

- carry out filling adjustments to make sure that the intended strength and quantity are achieved in practice
- allocate an identifying stock number to filled cases
- investigate any losses outside established loss patterns
- investigate all gains during the operation
- complete a declaration of outturn – if more than one size of bottle is to be filled, record the number of cases of each size
- secure any remnant
- complete your stock accounts
- keep a copy of the bottle label used
- keep a record if you use duty-free spirit for rinsing.

## Determining strength and volume

In order that the strength and volume of product may be determined for duty and stock control purposes, you must have a system in place that meets the requirements of Section 2 of ALDA, Regulation 31 of the Excise Warehousing (etc.) Regulations 1988 (EWER), and Regulations 18 and 19 of the Spirits Regulations 1991.

You may use any recognised method to determine alcoholic strength provided that the results are accurate and the method is used consistently. The method used to settle any dispute will depend on the type of product, for example, for spirit the method used will be the hydrometer referred to in the Spirit Regulations.

You must record alcoholic strength and volume as accurately as possible, ensuring that you adjust for any obscuration caused by the presence of sweetening, colouring or other ingredients. During an operation to bottle duty-suspended product in the warehouse, you must give prior notice of the intended strength and quantity per case (for example 12 × 40 per cent × 70cl = 3.36 litres of alcohol). You should take and record sufficient measurements during each operation of the liquid content and strength. You must keep a sample of each bottle label used and any other document which specifies the quantity and strength of the goods. You must be able to demonstrate that when measuring strength and volume you make a continuing genuine effort to achieve the strength and volume indicated on bottles or other containers.

HMRC will normally accept the labelled strength and volume as the basis of duty calculations if you can show that you are not aiming to achieve a higher strength than that shown on the label and that, if the actual strength exceeds the label strength, you take corrective action immediately. It may ask you to pay additional duty if it finds that you have packaged goods at strengths or volumes exceeding those on the labels.

## Excise warehouse returns (form W1)

All warehousekeepers with the exception of certain trade facility warehouses are required to submit a W1 stock return which shows stock movements and stock on hand at the end of the return period, normally on a monthly basis. Returns must be received within 14 days of the end of each return period. If you fail to submit a W1 return on time this may result in a financial penalty. If you persistently fail to submit returns it could result in the withdrawal of your authorisation.

# Appendix III: Notice 197

**Notice 197: Excise Goods: receipt into and removal from an excise warehouse of excise goods**

## General information

You may remove goods from an excise warehouse for:

- home use on payment of duty (sometimes referred to as 'released for consumption').
- dispatch under duty suspension to other approved UK warehouses, including those on the Isle of Man.
- dispatch under duty suspension to approved persons or premises in other EU Member States.
- export to non-EU countries in duty suspension.
- entitled miscellaneous removals.
- This list is not exhaustive. You should contact HMRC before removing goods from the warehouse for any other purpose unless we make a specific reference to that purpose in this notice or in your approval.

**You must observe certain rules before removal**:

- unless HMRC has agreed otherwise, take account of the goods to be removed and carry out any necessary examination.
- write the goods out of your stock account.
- ensure that duty is paid or accounted for on removals for home use.
- make sure that you supervise and check the removal is accurate before the goods leave the warehouse.
- In your own interests you should carry out sufficient checks to confirm that all your customers are genuine traders who are aware of their responsibilities in respect of excise goods.

You must individually record all removals for stock return

purposes and keep a schedule of different types of removals. If HMRC has restricted your approval to specific types of removals (for example, repacking operations and returning the goods to the original supplying warehouse), you may ask to remove goods for a different purpose, such as exports, by asking for a variation to your approval. The procedure for obtaining a variation is detailed in Notice 196. If you remove goods for purposes other than those in your approval, HMRC may revoke your approval.

All warehouses approved to store UK-produced whisky or whiskey must complete annual return Form W1A. The warehousekeeper, must provide details of the stock in warehouse at 31 December each year and information of movements made during the preceding year. HMRC will issue this form together with completion instructions.

## Removal to home use by duty payment (release for consumption)

You can only remove excise goods from your warehouse on payment of duty and within the conditions set out in your approval. You must take all necessary steps to pay the duty accurately and by the due dates. Failure to do so may result in prosecution or a financial penalty and could lead to restriction or withdrawal of your warehouse-keeper authorisation.

The systems, procedures and records to be kept and prepared when removing excise goods to home use will have been agreed at the time your approval and authorisation was granted. You must follow these procedures without exception. Before you remove goods to home use you must use the appropriate payment warrant documentation. This may be completed manually or online using either an online warrant or HMRC's XML service.

When payment is made by cash or equivalent, use warrants W5 for the removal of alcohol goods. When you are approved to defer payment of duty and wish to account for the duty using the deferment process, use warrant W5D. Paper warrants should be sent by post to the National Warrant Processing Unit (NWPU). Each warrant must contain a Consecutive Reference Number (CRN). HMRC strongly advises that you do not remove any goods until you are certain your warrant has been accepted. Copies of all forms and the notes to assist completion are available on the HMRC website.

HMRC also has a facility for the submission of remittance warrants and duty deferment warrants online, ATWD, available on the HMRC website. The online declaration service pre-populates standing data, including warehouse details, making it easier to complete the form and automatically calculates the amount of duty due as well as sub-totals, the amount of VAT, and the grand total. It also provides an immediate on-screen acknowledgement of receipt, confirms the approval of deferment warrants within a few minutes rather than having to wait for HMRC to reply by post, and provides a 24-hour service. To use the ATWD online service you will need to register and enrol for the service via the Government Gateway website.

The XML Direct Submission Service allows you to send data directly from your computer to HMRC. This allows you to submit large numbers of warrants directly from your duty management systems via XML, rather than re-keying the warrants on to an online screen. The XML format for exchanging information between computer systems is a stable and widely adopted technology but does not allow HMRC to access or interrogate your computer system, only to receive information, confirm receipt and pass back messages about invalid entries or format errors.

If you are not approved to use deferment arrangements, before removing goods from your warehouse you must complete cash remittance advice W5 and submit it to the NWPU together with your remittance. Remittances may take the form of cash; a banker's draft; a cheque covered by banker's standard guarantee (form C&E 307); a cheque individually guaranteed by the bank, endorsed 'guaranteed' or 'good', countersigned by the bank manager or other responsible official; BACS (for sums less than £20,000,000) or CHAPS. If you wish to pay by electronic transfer then you should contact the NWPU.

## Deferment of duty

To apply to defer daily payment of excise duty and make monthly direct debit payments, follow the guidance set out in Notice 101 Deferring Duty, VAT and Other Charges. Before your application is approved, you must take out a guarantee to cover your total monthly liabilities for the particular category of duty or VAT concerned. If you repeatedly exceed your guarantee level or deferment limit, your duty deferment facility will be suspended and may be withdrawn. If this happens you will be asked to make immediate cash payment and you will not be able to remove any goods until your payment has been received by the NWPU. You can provide supplementary guarantees to cover liabilities in periods of greater trade.

For all removals from your warehouse under deferred duty arrangements, you must make sure that the NWPU receives completed W5D and W6D forms for all that day's removals no later than the end of the following working day, unless HMRC has agreed scheduling arrangements. HMRC will confirm receipt by returning a stamped copy of the form, but the return of the copy only means that HMRC has received the form. In your own interests you may wish to delay removing the goods from your warehouse until you are sure that your deferment account has been debited.

## Denaturing (contaminating) and destroying alcohol

If any distillate held in duty suspension is surplus after

operations, of less value than the duty liable on it, or in an unmarketable condition, you may apply to HMRC for permission to denature (ie contaminate to make unpotable, usually with methanol) or destroy it without having to pay the duty. If someone else carries out the denaturing or destruction on your behalf, you remain responsible for ensuring that you comply with all HMRC procedures. You must give at least two working days' notice if you wish to carry out the procedure on your premises or five working days' notice if the procedure is to be conducted elsewhere.

You must inform HMRC why you wish to denature or destroy the goods, the description and quantity of the goods concerned, the potential amount of duty involved, the date, time and place of the proposed procedure, the proposed method and the purpose to which denatured product will be put. Notifications should be sent by email to niualcohol@ hmrc.gsi.gov.uk or by fax to 0141 555 3545. If HMRC decides that your proposed method of denaturing is not satisfactory it will tell you in writing. You are required to provide evidence that the goods have been denatured or destroyed in accordance with the notice given. Any discrepancies will be treated as a loss in warehouse.

Duty-paid goods may also be denatured or destroyed. To claim duty drawback, follow the directions set out in Notice 207.

## Calculation of excise duty

Unless HMRC has permitted the use of an alternative method that does not disadvantage the revenue, you must work out each constituent stage of the calculation process to a minimum of four decimal places. But to complete the remittance advice W5 or W5D, truncate the quantity of alcohol established at the end of the calculation process to two decimal places.

Please see the following examples.

(a) 800 cases of vodka, each containing 6x70cl @ 37.5% ABV
6 x 0.7 x 37.5 per cent = 1.575LPA x 800 = 1,260 x duty @
£28.74= £36,212.40

(b) 79 cases of whisky, each containing 12 x 70 cl x 43% ABV
12 x 0.7 x 43 per cent = 3.612LPA x 79 = 285.348LPA total x
£28.74 = £8,200.90.

(c) 1,209 cases of gin, each containing 12 x 1 litre x 40% ABV
12 x 1 x 40 per cent = 4.8 LPA x 1209 = 5803.2 LPA x £28.74 =
£166,783.96

# Appendix IV: Reviews and Appeals

**Reviews and appeals, stautes, HMRC contacts**

## Review and appeal procedures

When HMRC makes a decision you can appeal against, it will inform you and offer a review. It will explain the decision and tell you what you need to do if you disagree. Examples include the amount of an assessment, the issue of a civil penalty or a decision specifically connected to the relevant duty. You will usually have three options. Within 30 days you can send new information or arguments to the officer you have been dealing with, have your case reviewed by a different officer or have your case heard by an independent tribunal. A review will be handled by a different officer from the one who made the decision. If you prefer to have an independent tribunal hear your case, you must write directly to the Tribunals Service.

If you want HMRC to review a decision, you must write to the officer who issued the decision letter within 30 days of the date of the letter. HMRC will complete its review within 45 days unless it agrees another time-limit with you. If you have asked for a review you cannot ask the tribunal to hear your case until the 45 days (or the time-limit you agreed) has expired, or HMRC told you the outcome of its review. If you are not satisfied with the review's conclusion, you have 30 days to ask the tribunal to hear your case.

If you do not want a review you may appeal to the independent tribunal. You need to send your appeal to the Tribunals Service within 30 days of the date on the decision letter.

You can find further information about reviews and appeals in factsheet HMRC1 HMRC Decisions – 'What to do if you disagree'. You can download it from HMRC's website, or call the Revenue & Customs Orderline on 0300 200 3610. You can also find more information about how to appeal on the Tribunals Service website or by phoning 0845 223 8080.

## The Law

You will find the main primary, secondary, and European legal provisions governing the contents of HMRC Notices in:

- The Alcoholic Liquor Duties Act 1979 (ALDA)
- The Customs and Excise Management Act 1979 (CEMA)
- The Denatured Alcohol Regulations 2005 (SI 2005/1524)
- The Excise Duties (Deferred Payment) Regulations 1992 (SI 1992/3152)
- The Excise Goods (Drawback) Regulations 1995 (SI 1995/1046)
- The Excise Goods (Holding, Movement and Duty Point) Regulations 2010 (SI 2010/593)
- The Excise Warehousing (etc.) Regulations 1988 (SI 1988/809)
- The Revenue Traders (Accounts and Records) Regulations 1992 (SI 1992/3150)
- The Spirits (Rectifying, Compounding and Drawback) Regulations 1988 (SI 1988/1760)
- The Spirits Regulations 1991 (SI 1991/2564)
- The Warehousekeepers and Owners of Warehoused Goods Regulations 1999 (SI 1999/1278)
- European Council Directive 2008/118/EC OJ: L9, 14.01.09.

## Contacting HMRC

In most cases you should be able to find the information you need on the HMRC website, **www.hmrc.gov.uk**. If you cannot find the answer there, your first point of contact should be the Excise Helpline on 0300 200 3700.

If you have a problem with the EMCS registration and enrolment process, contact the EMCS Online Services Helpdesk on 0300 200 3701.

Contact details for other teams or offices mentioned in this Notice are:

**HMRC National Registration Unit (NRU)**
Portcullis House
21 India Street
Glasgow
G2 4PZ
Phone: 0141 555 3601
Fax: 0141 555 3506

**HMRC National Warrant Processing Unit (NWPU)/ National Warehouse Return Centre (NWRC)**
2nd Floor Portcullis House
13-21 India Street
Glasgow
G2 4PZ
Phone: 0141 555 3665
Fax: 0141 555 3555

**HMRC National Verification Centre (NVC)**
Portcullis House
21 India Street
Glasgow
G2 4PZ
Phone: 0141 555 3616

**HMRC Financial Securities Centre (FSC)**
Portcullis House
21 India Street
Glasgow
G2 4PZ Phone: 0141 555 3505
Fax: 0141 555 3506

# Appendix V: EC Regulation 110/2008

**EC Regulation 110/2008 Annex II: Categories of spirit drinks**

Although it describes itself as a regulation, this is actually a collection of all the relevant regulations from member states and therefore grows as the European Union grows. It is also subject to change – as when, for instance, 'Somerset cider brandy' was granted PGI status. The full-length version can be found by going to **www.spirits.eu**, clicking on 'internal market,' and selecting 'spirits definition and presentation' in the dropdown menu.

1. **Rum** is produced exclusively by alcoholic fermentation and distillation, either from molasses or syrup produced in the manufacture of cane sugar or from sugar-cane juice distilled at less than 96 per cent ABV, or by alcoholic fermentation and distillation of sugar-cane juice which has the aromatic characteristics specific to rum and a volatile substances content equal to or exceeding 225 grams per hectolitre of pure alcohol. The minimum strength of rum shall be 37.5 per cent ABV.

2. **Whisky or whiskey** is produced exclusively by distillation of a mash made from malted cereals with or without whole grains of other cereals, which has been saccharified by the diastase of the malt contained therein, with or without other natural enzymes, the final distillate matured for at least three years in wooden casks not exceeding 700 litres capacity. The minimum strength shall be 40 per cent ABV.

3. **Grain spirit** is produced exclusively by the distillation of a fermented mash of whole grain cereals. With the exception of Korn, the minimum strength of grain spirit shall be 35 per cent ABV.

4. **Wine spirit** is produced exclusively by the distillation of wine or wine fortified for distillation or by the redistillation of a wine distillate at less than 86 per cent ABV. The

minimum alcoholic strength by volume of wine spirit shall be 37.5 per cent ABV.

5. **Brandy** is produced from wine spirit, whether or not wine distillate has been added, distilled at less than 94.8 per cent ABV, matured for at least one year in oak receptacles or for at least six months in oak casks with a capacity of less than 1,000 litres. The minimum alcoholic strength of brandy shall be 36 per cent ABV. Brandy shall not be flavoured. This shall not exclude traditional production methods.

6. **Grape marc spirit** is produced exclusively from fermented and distilled grape marc. A quantity of lees may be added to the grape marc that does not exceed 25kg of lees per 100kg of grape marc used. The minimum alcoholic strength shall be 37.5 per cent ABV.

7. **Fruit marc spirit** is obtained exclusively by fermentation and distillation at less than 86 per cent ABV of fruit marc except grape marc. The maximum methanol content shall be 1,500g per hectolitre of pure alcohol. The minimum alcoholic strength shall be 37.5 per cent ABV.

8. **Raisin spirit or raisin brandy** is produced exclusively by the distillation of the product obtained by the alcoholic fermentation of extract of dried grapes of the Corinth Black or Moscatel varieties, distilled at less than 94.5 per cent ABV. It may only contain added caramel as a means to adapt colour.

9. **Fruit spirit** is produced exclusively by the alcoholic fermentation and distillation of fleshy fruit or must of such fruit, berries or vegetables, with or without stones, distilled at less than 86 per cent ABV, and in the case of stone-fruit spirits having a hydrocyanic acid content not exceeding 7g per hectolitre of pure alcohol. The minimum alcoholic strength by volume of fruit spirit shall be 37.5 per cent ABV.

10. **Cider spirit and perry spirit** are produced exclusively by the distillation at less than 86 per cent ABV of cider or perry. The minimum alcoholic strength shall be 37.5 per cent ABV.

11. **Honey spirit** is produced exclusively by fermentation and distillation of honey mash, distilled at less than 86 per cent ABV. The minimum alcoholic strength shall be 35 per cent ABV.

12. **Hefebrand or lees spirit** is produced exclusively by the distillation at less than 86 per cent vol. of lees of wine or of fermented fruit. The minimum alcoholic strength by volume of Hefebrand or lees spirit shall be 38 per cent ABV.

13. **Bierbrand or eau de vie de bière** is obtained exclusively by direct distillation under normal pressure of fresh beer. The minimum alcoholic strength of Bierbrand or eau de vie de bière shall be 38 per cent ABV.

14. **Topinambur or Jerusalem artichoke spirit** is produced exclusively by fermentation and distillation of Jerusalem artichoke tubers. The minimum alcoholic strength shall be 38 per cent ABV.

15. **Vodka** is produced from ethyl alcohol of agricultural origin obtained following fermentation with yeast from potatoes and/or cereals, or other agricultural raw materials, distilled and/or rectified so that the organoleptic characteristics of the raw materials used and by-products formed in fermentation are selectively reduced. This process may be followed by redistillation and/or treatment with appropriate processing aids, including activated charcoal, to give it special organoleptic characteristics. The minimum alcoholic strength by volume of vodka shall be 37.5 per cent ABV.

16. **Fruit spirit** obtained by maceration and distillation is produced by maceration of fruit or berries, whether partially fermented or unfermented, with the possible addition of a maximum of 20 litres of ethyl alcohol of agricultural origin or spirit and/or distillate deriving from the same fruit per 100kg of fermented fruit or berries. The minimum alcoholic strength shall be 37.5 per cent ABV.

17. **Geist** is obtained by maceration of unfermented fruits

and berries or vegetables, nuts, or other plant materials such as herbs or rose petals in ethyl alcohol of agricultural origin, followed by distillation at less than 86 per cent ABV. The minimum alcoholic strength shall be 37.5 per cent ABV.

18. **Gentian** is a distillate of gentian, obtained by the fermentation of gentian roots with or without the addition of ethyl alcohol of agricultural origin. The minimum alcoholic strength shall be 37.5 per cent ABV.

19. **Juniper-flavoured spirits** are produced by flavouring ethyl alcohol of agricultural origin and/or grain spirit and/or grain distillate with juniper. The minimum alcoholic strength shall be 30 per cent ABV.

20. **Gin** is a juniper-flavoured spirit drink produced exclusively by redistilling organoleptically suitable ethyl alcohol of agricultural origin of an appropriate quality with an initial alcoholic strength of at least 96 per cent ABV in stills traditionally used for gin, in the presence of juniper berries and of other natural botanicals provided that the juniper taste is predominant, or is a juniper-flavoured spirit drink produced by flavouring organoleptically suitable ethyl alcohol of agricultural origin with juniper berries. The minimum alcoholic strength shall be 37.5 per cent ABV. Only natural and/or nature-identical flavouring substances and/or flavouring preparations shall be used for the production of gin so that the taste is predominantly that of juniper.

21. **Distilled gin** is produced exclusively by redistilling organoleptically suitable ethyl alcohol of agricultural origin of an appropriate quality with an initial alcoholic strength of at least 96 per cent ABV in stills traditionally used for gin, in the presence of juniper berries and of other natural botanicals provided that the juniper taste is predominant; or the mixture of the product of such distillation and ethyl alcohol of agricultural origin with the same composition, purity and alcoholic strength. Natural and/or nature-identical flavouring substances and/or flavouring preparations may also be

used to flavour distilled gin. Gin obtained simply by adding essences or flavourings to ethyl alcohol of agricultural origin is not distilled gin. The minimum alcoholic strength shall be 37.5 per cent ABV.

22. **London gin** is a type of distilled gin obtained exclusively from ethyl alcohol of agricultural origin, with a maximum methanol content of 5g per hectolitre of pure alcohol, whose flavour is introduced exclusively through the redistillation in traditional stills of ethyl alcohol in the presence of all the natural plant materials used, the resultant distillate of which contains at least 70 per cent ABV. The minimum alcoholic strength shall be 37.5 per cent ABV.

23. **Caraway-flavoured spirits** are produced by flavouring ethyl alcohol of agricultural origin with caraway. The minimum alcoholic strength shall be 30 per cent ABV.

24. **Akvavit or aquavit** is a caraway and/or dillseed-flavoured spirit drink flavoured with a distillate of plants or spices. The minimum alcoholic strength shall be 37.5 ABV.

25. **Aniseed-flavoured spirits** are produced by flavouring ethyl alcohol of agricultural origin with natural extracts of star anise, anise, fennel, or any other plant which contains the same principal aromatic constituent, using one of the following processes or a combination thereof: maceration and/or distillation; redistillation in the presence of the seeds or other parts of the plants specified above; or addition of natural distilled extracts of aniseed-flavoured plants. The minimum alcoholic strength shall be 15 per cent ABV.

26. **Pastis** is an aniseed-flavoured spirit which also contains natural extracts of liquorice root, which implies the presence of the colorants known as chalcones as well as glycyrrhizic acid, the minimum and maximum levels of which must be 0.05 and 0.5g per litre. Pastis contains less than 100g of sugars per litre, and has a minimum and maximum anethole level of 1.5 and 2g per litre. The minimum alcoholic shall be 40 per cent ABV.

27. **Pastis de Marseille** is a pastis with an anethole content of 2g per litre. The minimum alcoholic strength shall be 45 per cent ABV.

28. **Anis** is an aniseed-flavoured spirit drink whose characteristic flavour is derived exclusively from anise and/or star anise and/or fennel. The minimum alcoholic strength shall be 35 per cent ABV.

29. **Distilled anis** contains alcohol distilled in the presence of the seeds referred to above, and in the case of geographical indications mastic and other aromatic seeds, plants or fruits, provided such alcohol constitutes at least 20 per cent of the alcoholic strength of the distilled anis. The minimum alcoholic strength shall be 35 per cent ABV.

30. **Bitters** are spirits with a predominantly bitter taste produced by flavouring ethyl alcohol of agricultural origin with natural and/or nature-identical flavouring substances. The minimum alcoholic strength shall be 15 per cent ABV.

31. **Flavoured vodka** is vodka which has been given a predominant flavour other than that of the raw materials. It may be sweetened, blended, flavoured, matured or coloured. The minimum alcoholic strength shall be 37.5 per cent ABV.

32. **Liqueur** is a spirit drink having a minimum sugar content of 70g per litre for cherry liqueurs the ethyl alcohol of which consists exclusively of cherry spirit; of 80g per litre for gentian or similar liqueurs prepared with gentian or similar plants as the sole aromatic substance; of 100g per litre in all other cases. Liqueur is produced by flavouring ethyl alcohol of agricultural origin or a distillate of agricultural origin or one or more spirit drinks or a mixture thereof, sweetened and with the addition of products of agricultural origin or foodstuffs such as cream, milk or other milk products, fruit, wine or aromatised wine. Nature-identical flavouring substances and preparations shall not be used in the preparation of the following liqueurs: blackcurrant,

cherry, raspberry, mulberry, bilberry, citrus fruit, cloudberry, arctic bramble, lingonberry, sea buckthorn, pineapple, mint, gentian, aniseed, genepi, vulnerary. The minimum alcoholic strength shall be 15 per cent ABV.

33. **Crèmes** (excluding milk products) are liqueurs with a minimum sugar content of 250g per litre. The minimum alcoholic strength shall be 15 per cent ABV.

34. **Crème de cassis** is a blackcurrant liqueur with a minimum sugar content of 400g per litre. The minimum alcoholic strength shall be 15 per cent ABV.

35. **Guignolet** is obtained by maceration of cherries in ethyl alcohol of agricultural origin. The minimum alcoholic strength shall be 15 per cent ABV.

36. **Punch au rhum** is a liqueur for which the alcohol content is provided exclusively by rum. The minimum alcoholic strength by volume of punch au rhum shall be 15 per cent ABV.

37. **Sloe gin** is a liqueur produced by maceration of sloes in gin with the possible addition of sloe juice. The minimum alcoholic strength shall be 25 per cent ABV.

38. **Sambuca** is a colourless aniseed-flavoured liqueur containing distillates of anise, star anise, or other aromatic herbs, with a minimum sugar content of 350g per litre. The minimum alcoholic strength shall be 38 per cent ABV.

39. **Maraschino**, Marrasquino or Maraskino is a colourless liqueur the flavour of which is given mainly by a distillate of marasca cherries or of the product obtained by macerating cherries or parts of cherries in alcohol of agricultural origin with a minimum sugar content of 250g per. The minimum alcoholic strength shall be 24 per cent ABV.

40. **Nocino** is a liqueur the flavour of which is given mainly by maceration and/or distillation of whole green walnuts with a minimum sugar content of 100g per litre. The minimum alcoholic strength shall be 30 per cent ABV.

41. **Egg liqueur** or advocaat or avocat or advokat is obtained

from ethyl alcohol of agricultural origin, distillate and/or spirit, the ingredients of which are egg yolk, egg white, and sugar or honey. The minimum sugar or honey content must be 150g per litre. The minimum content of pure egg yolk must be 140g per litre of the final product. The minimum alcoholic strength shall be 14 per cent ABV.

42. **Liqueur with egg** is obtained from ethyl alcohol of agricultural origin, distillate and/or spirit, the characteristic ingredients of which are egg yolk, egg white, and sugar or honey. The minimum sugar or honey content must be 150g per litre. The minimum egg yolk content must be 70g per litre of the final product. The minimum alcoholic strength shall be 15 per cent ABV.

43. **Mistrà** is a colourless spirit flavoured with aniseed or natural anethole with an anethole content of not less than 1 and not more than 2g per litre. It may also contain a distillate of aromatic herbs, but not added sugar. The minimum alcoholic strength shall be 40 per cent ABV and the maximum alcoholic strength 47 per cent ABV.

44. **Väkevä glögi or spritglögg** is produced by flavouring ethyl alcohol of agricultural origin with the natural or nature-identical aroma of cloves and/or cinnamon by maceration and/or distillation, redistillation of the alcohol in the presence of parts of the plants, addition of natural or nature-identical flavour of cloves or cinnamon or a combination of these methods. The minimum alcoholic strength shall be 15 per cent ABV.

45. **Berenburg or Beerenburg** is produced using ethyl alcohol of agricultural origin with the maceration of fruit or plants or parts thereof containing as specific flavour distillate of gentian root, juniper berries, and laurel leaves, which may be sweetened to a maximum of 20g per litre. The minimum alcoholic strength shall be 30 per cent ABV.

46. **Honey or mead nectar** is produced by flavouring a mixture of fermented honey mash and honey distillate and/

or ethyl alcohol of agricultural origin, and must contain at least 30 per cent fermented honey mash. The minimum alcoholic strength by volume of honey or mead nectar shall be 22 per cent ABV. Honey or mead nectar may be sweetened only with honey.

# Appendix VI: Trade and Professional Associations

## Wine & Spirit Trade Association

The rise of the craft distillery movement represents an exciting period for the spirits sector. Craft distillers offer consumers a locally produced product, with local flavours and a point of difference, which arouses interest and intrigue. The growing popularity of craft spirits also enables small, often first-time producers to enter the market, bringing a unique story to tell.

In the last 12 months, 251 million litres of spirits were sold in the UK at a value of over £9 billion. A significant proportion of these spirits are produced in the UK. For example, 93 per cent of gin sold in the UK is domestically produced. While craft spirits only make up a small proportion of total spirits sales, it is a growing category with huge potential. That's why the Wine & Spirit Trade Association is committed to helping the category grow by supporting craft distillers.

Whether you're interested in craft distilling as a hobby or as a new business venture it is important before starting your own craft distillery that you are aware of, and understand, the technical and regulatory environment. Navigating the myriad of UK and EU rules and regulations, from labelling to licensing, can be incredibly confusing, which is where the WSTA is uniquely placed to help members navigate the complexities of starting your own craft distillery.

The WSTA represents over 340 companies, large and small, producing, importing, exporting, transporting and selling wines and spirits in the United Kingdom. They campaign for a vibrant and sustainable wine and spirit industry, helping to build a future in which alcohol is produced, sold and enjoyed responsibly. They are unique in that we are the only trade association in the drinks industry to represent the entire supply chain. They work with members to help them grow and expand their business and offer advice on how to avoid costly and time-consuming hoops and hurdles.

This includes advice about the types of licences required to set up your distillery, how to move finished stock and how to go about establishing yourself as an export business. They offer advice on the most effective ways to defer paying excise duty and VAT and on the level of relationship you may need with logistics providers and warehouse keepers. They also advise on labelling issues and tariff classifications, depending on the exact specification of your product. Where you encounter legal or procedural obstacles, we can often advise and have access to other specialist services such as a free legal helpline, if required. We also run a fraud prevention unit.

The WSTA also maintains and builds close relationships with other trade associations across the EU and further abroad, to provide members with up-to-date information about legal and procedural developments affecting the sector and across international export markets.

They also provide members with the latest market information and consumer trends, tax advice, daily media updates, and discounts on certain goods and services including credit card payments; and run a range of committees which are tailored to members' needs. They produce a wide range of technical, legal and other publications – many of them exclusive to members – and host a number of events which offer unparalleled networking opportunities.

In other words they provide a one-stop shop of services for any would-be craft distiller. They believe that costs shouldn't be prohibitive to join the WSTA; therefore membership fees are set at £404 for companies with a turnover less than £500,000. For further information about the WSTA and the ranges of services  on offer go to **www.wsta.co.uk**.

# The Scotch Whisky Association

Scotch whisky is an iconic product recognised throughout the world. It is enjoyed by consumers in around 200 markets, from Asia to South America, the USA to France. When people buy Scotch they know they are getting a quality drink to be sipped and savoured.

The Scotch whisky industry is vital to the Scottish economy and society. Exports of Scotch are worth around £4 billion each year, 109 distilleries are licensed to operate in Scotland, and the industry supports 40,000 jobs across the UK. The industry provides employment across the country, often in economically fragile communities.

That success is largely down to the determination and hard work of Scotch whisky producers, but the Scotch Whisky Association (SWA), as the industry trade body, also has a vital role to play.

The SWA represents the wider interests of the industry. It advances the international interests and profile of Scotch whisky and all its member companies.

The Association has a long tradition of promoting and protecting the industry. It celebrated its centenary in 2012, having begun as the Wine & Spirit Brands Association in 1912 before becoming the Whisky Association in 1917 and ultimately the SWA in 1942.

For more than 100 years the Association has focused on protecting the industry, and has delivered a number of notable successes. It has made the case for fairer excise duty in the UK with 30 Chancellors of the Exchequer, taken legal action against thousands of 'fake whiskies', challenged tax and tariff discrimination overseas and helped the industry through war controls and Prohibition.

The Association remains as relevant today as it was when it was established last century in looking after the interests of a great industry.

## The SWA:

- Protects the integrity of Scotch whisky worldwide
- Promotes responsible attitudes to alcohol consumption
- Secures fair and equal access to international markets
- Tackles tax discrimination and secures appropriate regulation of the industry
- Secures a competitive manufacturing environment
- Promotes Scotch whisky as a quality product made from natural raw materials
- Promotes sustainable business practices
- Represents the industry's interests with governments at home and overseas.

Within the SWA there is a wealth of experience for members to draw on. By joining, companies get access to invaluable services, advice and expert analysis on a range of issues. The Association's priority is to support members of all sizes to let them grow their business. Its aim is to create the conditions for long-term growth worldwide and to secure Scotch whisky's place as the leading, high-quality spirit drink.

Here are examples of some of the SWA's areas of expertise.

### Protecting against fakes

The SWA takes action worldwide against the sale of local spirit 'dressed up' as Scotch whisky. Fakes result in a loss of genuine sales and cause reputational damage. The Association is very active in the fight against fakes – at any one time it is involved in around 70 legal actions and hundreds of investigations.

### Accessing and understanding international markets

The SWA works hard to ensure there is a level playing field to export Scotch Whisky around the world. It helps members expand overseas without discrimination.

## Securing a competitive operating environment

The SWA acts as the industry's focal point for all aspects of production and the supply chain, from the industry's raw materials needs through to customs and excise requirements. It co-ordinates the industry's award-winning Environmental Strategy.

## Raising the industry's profile and reaching governments

Scotch whisky attracts political and media interest from around the world. The SWA is the first point of contact for many external audiences and is as the voice of the industry. It also takes the lead on promoting social responsibility and issues around alcohol and health.

## A wealth of information

The Scotch whisky industry operates in an ever-changing global market-place. Companies need to have information at their fingertips and, in this respect, companies find the SWA's online knowledge base DRAMS, the members-only website, a vital resource.

## How to join:

To find out more about joining the SWA visit **www.scotch-whisky.org.uk/members-brands/** or email jbartholomew@swa.org.uk or call 0131 222 9200

# The Institute of Brewing & Distilling

The Institute of Brewing & Distilling or IBD is a members' organisation that is recognised worldwide in the professions of brewing and distilling. With around 4,500 members from 95 countries, the IBD is the largest global professional body for brewers and distillers and the only one that has a worldwide footprint.

The IBD's Vision Statement is: The advancement of

education and professional development in the science and technology of brewing, distilling and related industries.

The IBD offers a range of professional qualifications. They are (in increasing level of standard):

- Fundamentals of Distilling (FD)
- General Certificate in Distilling (GCD)
- General Certificate in Packaging of Spirits (GCP-S)
- General Certificate in Malting (GCM)
- Diploma in Distilling (Dipl. Distil)
- Diploma in Packaging (Dipl. Pack)

Recognised as global standards, these examinations are taken by more than 2,500 candidates every year at centres around the world. The IBD also runs residential study courses, workshops, symposia and an annual major brewing convention, either within the IBD Africa or Asia Pacific Sections. Every three years, a Worldwide Distilled Spirits Conference is also held, usually in Scotland.

*The Brewer & Distiller International* is a full-colour monthly members' magazine publishing technical, training and general interest articles, plus news and views. The Journal of the Institute of Brewing (JIB) is a quarterly scientific publication containing original research.

Membership of the IBD brings many advantages both to individual members and to their employers. Association with an international recognised professional body enhances a person's standing in his or her profession and provides opportunities for contact with professional colleagues in brewing, distilling, fermentation and allied industries. The examinations and membership of the IBD are recognised worldwide.

Global membership is administered on a geographical base with the following Sections around the world:

Africa • Asia Pacific • International • Irish • UK Great Northern • UK Midland • UK Scottish • UK Southern

## Member benefits include:

- Access to IBD qualifications
- Publications
- Training courses
- Section events
- Preferred members' rates at industry events such as IBD Conventions
- Access to the IBD website complete with online JIB and a wide range of industry information
- Visits to industry and academic establishments
- Industry networking and contact strategies
- Access to the IBD Learning Zone, making use of learning resources from our catalogue of publications
- Chartered Scientist: The Chartered Scientist (CSci) qualification is awarded to scientists who meet the high standards required and demands a commit ment to continuing professional development (CPD). It is intended to ensure high and improving standards across all scientific disciplines and reflects best practice in science. The IBD is licensed by the Science Council to award the status of Chartered Scientist to its members who reach the standards set and who complete an annual CPD report.

## Specific IBD qualifications for distillers

### Fundamentals of Distilling (FD)

This qualifications is suitable for all non-technical people employed in the distilling industry who would benefit from background knowledge in spirit production (such as Sales, Marketing, Finance or HR) and for those who have just commenced their technical or production careers. The FD takes the form of one multiple choice paper of 2 hours. The FD has City & Guilds accreditation at Level 2 of the National Qualification Framework in the UK (or equivalent internationally recognised standards).

**General Certificate in Distilling (GCD)**
**General Certificate in Packaging of Spirits (GCP-S)**
These qualifications are a measure of the basic knowledge (theoretical and practical) underpinning, distilling, packaging and associated operations within the distilling industry. They are appropriate for team members, team leaders and technicians. These General Certificates can be an end in themselves, or the start of professional development leading to the IBD Diploma in Distilling. The General Certificates take the form of one multiple choice paper of two hours. GCD candidates can choose from three options; cereal, grape or molasses. The General Certificates have City & Guilds accreditation at Level 3 of the National Qualifications Framework in the UK (or equivalent internationally recognised standards).

**Diploma in Distilling (Dipl. Distil)**
The examination is a measure of the candidates' theoretical knowledge of science and technology of distilling, and typical candidates are team leaders, operational managers and technicians. The exam is split into three modules, which can be sat in any order and combination.
- Module 1 – Materials and Wort
- Module 2 – Fermentation, Distillation & Maturation
- Module 3 – Process Technology

Each question paper is three hours in duration, and requires short and essay-style answers. The Dipl. Distl has City & Guilds accreditation at Level 4 of the National Qualifications Framework in the UK (or equivalent internationally recognised standards).

For more details on the Institute of Brewing and Distilling's qualifications or training, or for details on how to become a member, visit them at **www.ibd.org.uk**

# The Gin Guild

The Gin Guild is an industry body composed of both large and small gin distillers and brand owners, and represents the gin industry as a whole. It aims to promote the gin category across the globe, enhancing its image and widening its appeal to worldwide consumers, and to ensure that gin grows its share of the spirit market. It brings together gin distillers and industry leaders involved in the production, promotion, distribution and consumption of gin and promotes and encourages commitment to excellence in gin distillation and industry custodianship of the spirit category.

The Guild does not seek to promote any particular branded product or products but aims to bring the widest range of products and their producers – and those associated in the wider industry – together in order to provide a valued forum for all those involved in gin production, sales, marketing and distribution.

The Guild is part of the Worshipful Company of Distillers, one of London's oldest historical trade bodies, incorporated by Royal Charter in 1638, whose historical role was to hold key responsibilities for the control and regulation of early gin distillers. That provides a unique historical link to the gin industry that places London at the historic heart of the modern gin category and industry

The Worshipful Company of Distillers aims, via the work of The Gin Guild, to provide and facilitate a wider opportunity for those involved in the gin industry to network and socialise in the gin industry, reflecting and including many of the traditions of the City. The Guild also has a developing role in education. This includes education and information for the industry, with key events being filmed for future reference and industry use, via the member section of the Guild website. Education also includes, bar staff 'gin serve and awareness' training, as well as consumer-facing information and media profile liaison.

## Membership

Membership is open to a range of gin industry players. The classes of membership include:

Warden Rectifiers: This group is limited to producer/ distillers and brand owners (excluding supermarket own brands and retail off-trade, and/or ineligible gin styles, and smaller low volume craft distillers). This is held as a corporate representative position (with only one such position in each company).

Rectifiers: Individuals involved with the wider gin industry (including craft distillers and those involved in production, distribution, marketing sales, bar staff, retailers/buyers, journalists, educators and other commentators).

The installations of the Grand Rectifier, Wardens and other members of the Guild are by way of solemn ceremonies, reflecting the traditions of the trade guilds of the City of London. Guild members receive a certificate of admission to the Guild, a silver Guild 'juniper sprig' insignia and a commemorative Guild plaque.

## Activities

The Guild arranges, co-host and/or facilitates access for Guild members to a programme of gin-related events and celebrations. These include Guild installation ceremonies (including an option for full members of Guild installation at the prestigious Mansion House, London, followed by the Worshipful Company of Distillers Banquet in the famous Egyptian Hall).

The Gin Guild represents gin distillers and brand owners (subject to the proviso that the gins concerned must be distilled and not cold-compounded). Small craft distillers often join in an individual capacity as Rectifiers, but several craft distillers and small brands who have seen their businesses expand and grow have already achieved Warden status. Warden status entitles the company to two representatives, one holding the corporate capacity of Warden and one being the Warden Nominated Rectifier.

The Gin Guild has recognised that within the wide range of skills and experience its members at all levels enjoy an unparalleled networking access to those in the gin industry and those associated with that industry, indeed the Gin Industry Annual Dinner regularly brings together the largest number of such players ever seen in the UK.

Peer to peer exchange between smaller craft distillers in particular has specifically been recognised by the Gin Guild as providing a very useful function. This allows such distillers to be able to have a frank exchange between them and to share problems and solutions that due to completion etc would not be possible with the long established players who have already carved out a niche in the gin trade.

This niche networking, alongside Guild plans to provide additional show case opportunities to expose and promote members gins as part of a general gin and gin serve promotion, is especially valuable to those brands who do not have the generous marketing budgets enjoyed by some of their larger brethren.

The Gin Guild has an informative web presence, which is regularly updated. This as stated includes film clips of useful training and educational materials. Some of these are open and others, with more detailed content, are only available for members.

For more details, contact the Guild Director General (details at **www.theginguild.com**) Tel. 020 3397 2737.

## The Scottish Craft Distillers Association

The craft distilling movement has been much slower to form a trade association than the pioneering microbrewers, who came together to found the Small Independent Brewers Association (now the Society of Independent Brewers) in the early 1980s. The main reason for this is that there is none of the antagonism between established distillers and parvenus that characterised the relationship between mainstream brewers and micros; and the main reason for this, in turn, is that the big distillers don't control the retail trade in the way that the brewers did via the tied estates that almost monopolised the pub trade.

In England, the Craft Distillers Alliance was wound up in late 2014 after three years during which it achieved much but, without external funding or support and entirely dependent on volunteers, found itself unable to thrive. At the same time as the CDA was winding up, however, a new industry body – the Scottish Craft Distillers Association – was being created north of the border in very different circumstances.

SCDA started as one of the Common Interest Groups brought together by Interface Food & Drink, a joint body created by the Scottish universities, Scottish Enterprise and Scottish food and drink industry bodies to offer funding and support to innovators in the industry. The Group soon saw the advantages of creating a formal association that would in time be able to represent its members at overseas trade events they would otherwise have been unable to attend, and to create a widely-recognised accreditation scheme that would establish 'craft distilled in Scotland' almost as a brand in its own right. SCDA also aims to reduce its members' costs by co-operating in bulk buying, sharing transport costs and setting up common bottling and internet trading facilities.

The Association rapidly recruited more than 60 members,

including 23 distilleries either up and running or going through the licensing process. Many of the distiller members are English, and under SCDA's draft constitution have full access to its services but no voting rights. It is envisaged that a separate and fully-constituted branch for English, Welsh and Northern Irish distillery companies will be created in due course.

At time of writing SCDA is not formally fully constituted, but membership rates have been set at £50 for individual members and £150 for corporate members and allied trades. Membership enquiries are welcomed through its Facebook page at **https://www.facebook.com/ ScottishCraftDistillers**. The Association chairman is Tony Reeman-Clark of Strathearn Distillery.

# Directory of services and suppliers

## Bottles, bottling equipment, labelling, & packaging

**Ardagh Group Glass**
Portland Road, Irvine KA128JA
**Tel** 01294 278641
**www.ardaghgroup.com**

**Beatson Clark**
The Glass Works, Greasbrough
Road, Rotherham S60 1TZ
**Tel** 01709 828 141
**www.beatsonclark.co.uk**

**CS Labels**
Unit D, Willenhall Trading
Estate, Midacre, West Midlands
WV13 2JW
**Tel** 01902 365840
**www.cslabels.co.uk**

**Enterprise Tondelli**
Unit 7, College Farm Buildings,
Barton Rd, Pulloxhill, Beds
MK45 5 HP. Tel 01525 718288
**www.enterprisetondelli.com**

**Garthwest Corrugated
Cardboard**
Rotterdam Rd, Sutton Fields,
Hull HU7 0XA.
**Tel** 01482 825121
**www.garthwest.com**

**Gavin Watson Labels**
79-109 Glasgow Rd, Glasgow
G72 0LY.
**Tel** 01698 826000
**www.gavinwatson.co.uk**

**Graphic Packaging
International**
Filwood Rd, Fishponds, Bristol
BS16 3SB
**Tel** 07771 901493
**www.graphicpkg.com**

**Hamilton Adhesive Labels Ltd**
Unit B, Interlink Way South,
Coalville, Leicestershire
LE67 1PG
**Tel** 01530 518010
**www.hamilton-labels.co.uk**

**Krones UK**
Great Bank Rd, Wingates Ind
Est, Westhoughton, Lancs
BL5 3XB.
**Tel** 01942 845000
**www.krones.de**

**Label Apeel Ltd**
James House, Murrayfield Road,
Leicester LE3 1UW
**Tel** 0116 231 4555
**www.labelapeel.co.uk**

**O-I Glass UK**
Edinburgh Way, Harlow, Essex
CM20 2DB
**Tel** 01279 422222
**www.O-I.com**

**Olympus Labels**
Olympus House, Grangefield
Industrial Estate, Pudsey
LS28 6QW
**Tel** 0113 236 3283
**www.olympuslabels.co.uk**

**Rankin Brothers**
Unit 3C, Drakes Farm, Drakes
Drive, Aylesbury, Bucks
HP18 9BA
**Tel** 01844203100
**www.rankincork.co.uk**

**Spear Labels UK**
Christopher Grey Court,
Llantarnam Industrial Park,
Cwmbran NP44 3SE
**Tel** 01633 627600
**www.spearinc.com**

**Vigo Ltd**
Dunkeswell, Honiton, Devon,

EX14 4LF
**Tel** 01404 892100
**www.vigoltd.com**

**William Croxson & Son Ltd**
Alpha Place, Garth Road,
Morden, Surrey SM4 4LX
**Tel** 0208 337 2945
**www.croxsons.com**

## Contract distillers

**Alcohols Ltd**
Charrington's House North,
The Causeway, Bishop's
Stortford CM23 2ER
**Tel** 01279 658464
**www.alcohols.co.uk**

**English Spirit Distillery**
The Old Salt Depot, Brinkley
Road, Dullingham, Newmarket
CB8 9UW
**Tel** 01638 507981
**www.englishspiritdistillery.com**

**Essential Drinks**
Melbury Park, Clayton Road,
Warrington WA3 6PH
**Tel** 01925 286400
**www.essential-drinks.com**

**Haymankimia**
70 Eastways Park, Witham,
Essex CM8 3YE

Tel 01376 517517/535900
**www.hayman-distillers.co.uk**

**Thames Distillers**
Timbermill Way, Gauden Road,
London SW4 6LY
Tel 0207 720 4747.
**www.thamesdistillers.co.uk**

## Distillery equipment, consultancy & installation

**Allen Associates**
Stirling, FK9 4NF
Tel 01786 448777
**www.allenhpe.co.uk**

**Briggs of Burton**
Burton on Trent, Staffordshire,
DE14 2LH
Tel 01283 566661
**www.briggsplc.co.u**k

**John Dore & Co**
1 Farnham Rd, Guildford,
Surrey GU2 4RG
Tel 01483 549816
**www.johndore.co.uk**

**Exigo Brewing & Distilling**
4 Westleigh Business Park,
Winchester Ave, Blaby, Leics
LE8 4EZ
Tel 0116 277 0077
**www.exigobad.com**

**Forsyths**
Rothes, Banffshire AB38 7AD
Tel 01340 831787
**www.forsyths.com**

**McMillan Coopersmiths & Fabricators**
Prestonpans Industrial Estate
Prestonpans, EH32 9JB
Tel 01875 811110
**www.mcmillanltd.co.uk**

**Speyside Cooperage**
Dufftown Rd, Craigellachie,
Banffshire AB38 9RS
Tel 01340 871108
www.speysidecooperage.co.uk

## Distribution & wholesale

**National Drinks Distributors**
Yeoman House, 16 The Green,
Aston-on-Trent, Derbys
DE72 2AA
Tel 01332 793085
**www.nationaldrinks.com**

## Institutions & training providers

**Bonded Warehousekeepers' Association**
PO Box 29089, Dunfermline
KY11 9WB
Tel 07736 633162

www.thebwa.com
**British Bottlers Institute**
53 Basepoint, Andover, Hants
SP10 3FG
**Tel** 01264 326478
**www.bbi.org.uk**

**British Food & Beverage
Industry Suppliers Association**
3 Brewery Road , Wolverhampton, West Midlands WV1 4JT
**Tel** 01902 422303
**www.bfbi.org.uk**

**Institute of Brewing &
Distilling**
33 Clarges St, London W1J 7EE
**Tel** 0207 499 8144
**www.ibd.org.uk**

**International Centre for
Brewing & Distilling**
ICBD, Heriot-Watt University,
Riccarton, Edinburgh EH14 4AS
**Tel** 0131 449 5111
**www.hw.ac.uk**

**Scotch Whisky Association**
20 Atholl Crescent, Edinburgh
EH3 8HF
**Tel** 0131 222 9200
**www.scotch-whisky.org.uk**

**Scottish Craft Distillers
Association**

Douglas Watson, Secretary
**Tel** 01997 421753
**Mob** 07831 138626
Email membership@scottish-craftdistillers.org

**The Gin Guild**
The Gimlet, 199 New London
Rd, Chelmsford, Essex CM2 0AP
**Tel** 0203 397 2737
**www.theginguild.com**

**Wine & Spirit Education Trust**
International Wine & Spirit
Centre, 39 Bermondsey St,
London SE1 3XF
**Tel** 0207 089 3800
**www.wset.co.uk**

**Wine & Spirit Trade
Association**
International Wine & Spirit
Centre, 39 Bermondsey St,
London SE1 3XF
**Tel** 0207 089 3877
**www.wsta.co.uk**

## Laboratory, analytical, & technical services

**Anton Paar**
Unit F, The Courtyard, St Albans
AL4 0LA
**Tel** 01992 514730
**www.anton-paar.com**

**Lovibond Colour Measurement**
Lovibond House, Solstice Park,
Amesbury SP4 7SZ
**Tel** 01980 664800
**www.lovibondcolour.com**

**QCL**
Forest Row, East Sussex,
RH18 5DW
**Tel** 01342 820820
**www.qclscientific.com**

**Tatlock and Thomson Ltd**
Tatlock House, The Teuchats,
By Leven, Fife KY8 5PF
**Tel** 01333 360 603/627
**www.tatlockandthomson.com**

## Raw materials &
## consumables

**AB Mauri UK and Ireland**
Barn Way, Lodge Farm Industrial
Estate, Northampton NN5 7UW
**Tel** 01604 755522
**www.abmauriukandireland.com**

**Abbey Botanicals**
3 The Wylde, Leinthall Earls,
Herefs HR6 9TU
**Tel** 01568 770832
**www.abbeybotanicals.co.uk**

**Alcohols Ltd**
Charrington's House North, The

Causeway, Bishop's Stortford
CM23 2ER
**Tel** 01279 658464
**www.alcohols.co.uk**

**Baird's Malt**
Station Maltings, Witham, Essex
CM8 2DU
**Tel** 01376 513566
**www.bairds-malt.co.uk**

**Beacon Commodities**
Middleton Lane, Lewes Rd,
Westmerton, Sussex BN6 8RL
**Tel** 01273 844264
**www.beaconcommodities.com**

**Blue Sky Botanics**
Castle Farm, Upton Bishop,
Ross-on-Wye, Herefs HR9 7UW
**Tel** 01989 780486
**www.blueskybotanics.com**

**Boortmalt UK**
Locations: Glenesk, Buckie,
Bury St Edmunds, Knapton
**Tel** 01542 8374012
**www.boortmalt.com**

**Crisp Maltings Group**
Gt Ryburgh, Fakenham, Norfolk
NR21 7AS
**Tel** 01328 829391
**www.crispmalt.com**

**DD Williamson (UK)**
Trafford Park Road,
Manchester M17 1PA
**Tel** 0161 886 3345
**www.ddwilliamson.co.uk**

**Edwin Tucker & Sons**
The Maltings, Teign Rd, Newton
Abbot, Devon TQ12 4AA
**Tel** 01626 334002
**www.edwintucker.co.uk**

**French & Jupps**
Stanstead Abbots, Ware,
Herts SG12 8HG
**Tel** 01920 870015
**www.frenchandjupps.co.uk**

**Hayman Distillers**
70 Eastways Park, Witham,
Essex CM8 3YE
**Tel** 01376 517517 / 535900
**www.hayman-distillers.co.uk**

**Kanegrade Ltd**
Ingredients House, Caxton Way,
Stevenage, Herts SG1 2DF
**Tel** 01438 742242
**www.kanegrade.com**

**Lallemand Yeast**
Dallow Street, Burton-upon-
Trent, Staffs DE14 2PQ
**Tel** 01283 563268
**www.lallemandbds.com**

**Muntons**
Cedars Maltings, Stowmarket,
Suffolk IP14 2AG
Tel 01449 618300
**www.muntons.com**

**Simpsons Malt**
Tweed Valley Malting,
Tweedsside Trading Estate,
Berwick-upon-Tweed TD15 2UZ
**Tel** 01289 330033
**www.simpsonsmalt.co.uk**

**StarSpice Ingredients Ltd**
The Old Manse, High St,
Fowlmere, Cambs SG8 7ST
**Tel** 01763 208252
**www.starspice.co.uk**

**Thos Fawcett & Sons**
Eastfield Lane, Castleford, W
Yorks WF10 4LE
**Tel** 01997 552490

**Warminster Maltings**
39 Pound St, Warminster,
Wilts BA12 8NN
Tel 01985 212014
**www.warminster-malt.co.uk**

# Index